# Don't Ask Me!

# DON'T ASK ME!

## The enigma of why
# SHEILA STEAFEL
### is attracted to BASTARDS...

fantom
publishing

First published in 2012 in hardback under the title *Bastards*
by Fantom Publishing, an imprint of Fantom Films
This paperback edition first published by Fantom in 2019
www.fantompublishing.co.uk

A catalogue record for this book is available from the British Library.

Hardback ISBN: 978-1-78196-020-2
Paperback ISBN: 978-1-78196-349-4

Typeset by Phil Reynolds Media Services, Leamington Spa
Printed and bound in the UK by ImprintDigital.com

Photography and cover design by Dexter O'Neill

For Arnold Wesker, playwright,
who strictly speaking doesn't qualify to be
mentioned under this title

# CONTENTS

**bastard** (ˈbɑːstəd, ˈbæs-)

- *Informal, offensive.* an obnoxious or despicable person.
- *Informal.* something extremely difficult or unpleasant.
- something irregular, abnormal or inferior.
- *Old-fashioned or offensive.* illegitimate by birth.

Collins English Dictionary

# A TRAGEDY

by Sheila Steafel (aged 13)

The nobles round the table sat
With food and wine in plenty,
And laughed and joked in drunken mirth
Their glasses never empty.

Then to the hall (unseen by all)
A servant swiftly ran
And whispered to his master that
Outside… there was a man!

"What is his name? Whence does he come?
And what does he desire?"
"His name's El Staine, he comes from Spain,
His need of food is dire!"

"Send him away!" the master cried,
Full wrath at this intrusion,
"I'll have no strangers dining here!
(Humph!)
A fanciful illusion!"

*Don't Ask Me!*

One year after this dreadful scene
Of malice from this peer
He stricken was with a disease
And courtiers left in fear.

At length a doctor of renown
Was summoned to his bed,
And with a wrinkled, furrowed brow,
He thought a while, then said:

"It was some years ago, my lord,
In Spain there lived a fellow
Who found a cure for this disease
In tablets pink and yellow.

He made a shipload of these pills,
Spent all his money thereon,
But it did sink, and with it too
His wealth and riches were gone.

He came out here some years ago
As poor as any church mouse,
His name was Staine. I hear he died
Of hunger in the poorhouse!"

The noble started from his bed,
"I remember that name!" he cried,
"I rue the day I said him Nay!"
The sinner fell back... and died.

So when you're feasting next, my friend,
Think of the saints who've fasted.
Be generous or you might die
Like him, a lonely bastard.

Teacher's comment:

> *A good effort, shows promise. Suggest you replace last noun with something less offensive.*

Well, I didn't replace it. After all, even at that young age, to my mind the noble's behaviour *was* offensive, which made him… well, a bastard.

# INTRODUCTION

When I read through the final draft of my autobiography, I decided to take out several anecdotes about my personal life simply because they seemed a sort of indulgence, and didn't add to what I wanted to say about my life and my career. They were hiccups along the way with some attacks worse than others, but all were finally 'got rid' (as my cousin Lillian used to say). I put them in a file which I called BASTARDS for my own amusement and thought no more about them until my book came out and I was being asked what my next writing project would be. For want of anything else to say I would reply BASTARDS, and the response was so positive that what had started as a whim began to take on substance.

So here it is. Since you ask (and you will) the bastards were all my own. Some were short, as are some of the tales, and some tall, which, in spite of your incredulity, none of the tales are. Well, I've said it before and I'll say it again, I couldn't make them up.

Could I?

# LEONARD

Like all little girls should, when I was thirteen I fell in love with the boy next door. His name was Leonard. On the day he moved in I happened to be sitting on the high red-brick wall (my favourite vantage point) that fronted our suburban house in Johannesburg, and I watched as an old, battered blue van, its rear doors barely held together by an inadequate rope against the push of domestic paraphernalia, struggled its way along the hot tarmac road and groaned to a halt outside the unoccupied house next door. A boy of about fifteen threw open the passenger door and levered himself onto the ground. His left leg was encased in a large plaster cast, and he pulled a pair of steel crutches after him. Noticing me, he tucked the crutches firmly under his armpits, and chortling with glee proceeded to use them as stilts, taking giant strides up the gravel path at the side of the house and back again, sending the small, sharp stones spraying in all directions.

'Stop that, Leonard!'

A large woman climbed down awkwardly from the van. 'Go inside and open the windows. Here, come and get the key!'

Ignoring her he continued his performance, showing off, I decided, for my benefit… and indeed I was duly impressed: there was no doubting his skill. By now the driver, a short, paunchy man with a balding head, was tugging at the rope.

'Never mind the keys,' he called irritably, 'get over here, Leonard, and give me a hand!'

The boy skidded to a halt just below me and looked up.

'That's me,' he drawled, 'Leonard.'

'I'm Elsa,' I replied. He smiled a slow, lopsided smile, and for some reason my heart lurched.

'Well, I'll be seeing you… Elsa.'

And the way he said my name, drawing out each syllable, made me catch my breath. It was love at first sight.

For the next week or so after school I made a point of hanging around outside the house hoping to see him, and at first we met up seemingly by chance, and soon by choice. I would perch on the wall, and he would sit astride the wooden gate at the end of the gravel path, balancing a crutch on the ground to keep him steady. Later, when the plaster cast was removed and my first shyness had evaporated, he would sit on the wall beside me under the bluest of African skies, and it wasn't long before we were confiding in one another. Leonard told me he was the only child of a loveless marriage. He adored his Catholic mother whom he considered his best friend, and he hated his father, a Jewish travelling salesman with a sour disposition and a quick temper. Leonard's mother feared him as did Leonard himself, and the atmosphere when he was around was uneasy.

'He doesn't hit you, does he?' I asked.

'He used to, but he doesn't any more. I'm too quick for him,' he said, and he smiled his wicked, lopsided smile.

It soon became clear that his father was seldom at home, and I could always tell when he was there, because the curtains, usually left open, would be closed, and the house seemed to turn in on itself.

As time went by I looked forward more and more to being with Leonard. I would watch out for him coming home, listening for his footsteps on the gravel path, and then stroll out nonchalantly for a chat. Leonard was tall, and lanky, and mature for his age. He had a slow way of speaking, a sort of drawl that intrigued and thrilled me. He would pause mid-sentence, give an odd little chuckle, and then continue. I loved his crinkly blonde hair and the two pointy lower teeth that only showed when he smiled, giving him a slightly demonic look, and I loved the curious way his little fingers curved inwards.

Leonard had a best friend called Ian, a wiry lad with a shock of ginger hair and a raucous laugh. He often came home with Leonard after school when his father was away, and when he did, much to my chagrin I would be given a peremptory wave as they headed inside the house, and soon some current popular record or other would blare out through the open sitting-room window. His mother didn't seem to mind the racket even though these sessions often continued late into the night, and I discovered that by standing on a stool pulled up to the bathroom window I could see into the brightly lit sitting room next door. I would spy on them as they jigged about in some sort of demented dance, or swilled cans of beer, lolling on a bulky old sofa. I positively ached to join them, but all I could do was watch, and worship.

Now and again Leonard and I would arrange to meet after school at Dino's, a local café, all steel and formica and dark, cool booths. Dino, the forty-something proprietor, was the son of Greek immigrants. He had started out as an amateur heavyweight boxer with a promising future, but a motorcycle accident had put paid to his dreams. In spite of this setback he still kept up with what training he could, and each day found him behind his gleaming counter, squat and square and at the ready. The wall behind him was covered in framed photographs of himself as a young pugilist being embraced by managers and friends and fellow boxers. They were scrawled over with effusive dedications, and should an unwary customer show the slightest interest or curiosity, Dino, shirt sleeves rolled up high over impressively muscular biceps, would wave them into one of the stools at the counter, and with the bribe of a complimentary piece of confection ('No, please, take, take… is my pleasure!'), recount his triumphs and tell of undying friendships. Leonard had discovered Dino's

Achilles' heel early on, and in spite of knowing the anecdotes almost as well as Dino himself, by the time I arrived more often than not Leonard would be sitting at the counter hanging onto the proprietor's every word as he happily munched on his bribe. Sliding into our favourite booth we would catch up on any news, and when the flashing jukebox blared out, instead of struggling to make ourselves heard over the throb, we would sit sucking up our deliciously sweet, thick ice-cream milkshakes through candy-striped straws, content just to be in one another's company.

Leonard's life was an exciting mystery to me. He kept odd hours, sometimes coming home late at night, often missing school, and even disappearing for days at a time, and it was on one of these occasions that I first met his mother. I hadn't seen Leonard around for a few days, and one late afternoon I was about to give up my vigil on the wall and head indoors when his mother emerged from the house. She strolled down the path, stopping for a moment to light a cigarette. Matronly, solid, and of average height, she wore a faded floral overall that strained across her full bosom. When she reached me she stopped, pulled strongly on the cigarette, and, looking up at me with half-closed eyes, blew out a slow stream of smoke.

'You must be Elsa,' she said. Her voice was low, with the husky rasp that identifies a heavy smoker.

'Yes, I am.'

The woman coughed briefly and reached up a hand. 'I'm Betty, Leonard's mother. He's told me a lot about you. Nice to meet you at last.'

I had previously only seen Leonard's mother at a distance. Looking down at her now I was surprised to see that in spite of the few lines etched in her face, she was younger than I had expected. Her skin was pale, emphasising the dark shadows under her eyes, and she had tied her faded blonde hair back with a brown shoelace. I took the proffered hand; it felt dry and rough, the grip strong.

'If you're waiting for Leonard he's not here, and I doubt if he'll be back tonight. Tomorrow maybe.'

'Oh.' I couldn't hide my disappointment and I wasn't sure whether it was wise to ask, but curiosity got the better of me. 'Where's he gone?'

Leonard's mother dragged again on the cigarette, drawing the smoke deep into her lungs, choking a little as she exhaled.

'Dunno,' she said, unconcerned, 'he never tells me and I never ask. I did ask him once and he didn't like that. But I don't worry about him, not any more. He knows what he's doing, does my Lennie. He's a good son, a good boy. And he looks after me, know what I mean?'

She winked conspiratorially, and although I wasn't quite sure what she meant I nodded and we laughed. There was something about her, a warmth that made me feel she was already a friend, with no age gap between us.

'Anyway,' she continued, 'he's never away for more than three days at a time, so he's bound to be back by tomorrow. Nice break for me, though,' she added conspiratorially, 'both of them away and only myself to bother with.'

'Elsa! For Heaven's sake, what are you doing out there?'

My mother had appeared at our front door.

'Haven't you got any homework to do?' Her voice sounded more irritable than usual.

'Coming!'

I muttered an apology as I scrambled down from my perch.

'Time I went in anyway,' said my new friend, grinding her cigarette butt into the gravel, 'and don't you worry about Lennie, he knows what he's doing… you'll find that out when you get to know him better!'

As it happened, any ideas of my getting to know Leonard better were firmly scotched by my mother that night. She put her head around my bedroom door as I lay in bed reading, the book propped up on my chest.

'Can I come in for a minute? I need to talk to you about something important.'

'Okay,' I said, my eyes firmly fixed on the page.

She sat on the side of the bed.

'What are you reading?' she asked, though we both knew it wasn't my choice of literature that was on her mind.

'*Forsyte Saga*,' I answered, still not looking at her.

'Enjoying it?'

I put the book down with a sigh and waited.

'Alright,' said my mother, 'it's about those new people next door. That woman you were talking to this afternoon... I believe her husband is Jewish, but she isn't, she's a Catholic.'

'Yes, I know, and she's a really nice person,' I said defensively. 'I'm sure if you got to know her...'

'Good Lord, I don't want to know her. The last thing in the world I want is to socialise with them. He's married out.'

'I'm not saying socialise with them. Her husband's never there anyway. But you and her might have things in common.'

'Things in common? With a woman like that?' my mother exploded. 'What on earth are you talking about?'

'Well, she and him... her husband... I don't think they get on too well, and you and dad... I mean...' The unfinished sentence hung in the air between us and I wished I had never started. When my mother spoke again her voice was low and threatening.

'Have you been discussing me with her? Is that what you were talking about? Me and your father?'

'No, of course not!' I managed, my heart beginning to race.

My mother pulled the book out of my hands, and for a frightening moment I thought she was going to strike me with it. Instead she slammed it shut and held it clamped in both hands.

'Now you listen to me. Don't you ever discuss what goes on between me and your father with anyone, do you hear me? No one! It is nobody's business but our own, understand? Do you understand?'

I nodded, too confused and afraid to speak.

'Your father and I may have our differences, but let me tell you, there is one thing we most certainly agree about, and that is your so-called friendship with that boy next door. We've discussed it and decided that from now on you will not see or talk to him, is that understood? We are forbidding you to see him or talk to him again.'

'But why...' I tried to continue but my throat was tight, and although I tried to stop the welling tears, they spilled down my cheeks.

'Why? Because... stop that crying and listen to me... because,' she spoke slowly and deliberately, as though I were simple-minded, 'because his mother is a Catholic, and that makes him a Catholic. A non-Jew! We have never allowed you to go out with a non-Jewish boy, and we have no intention of letting you start now.'

It was true. All the boys I knew socially were part of the circle belonging to our synagogue, and although I had had a brief crush on a boy called Leon, and held hands in the dark of a cinema with another boy called Martin, Leonard was different. He was the most interesting, the most mysterious person I had ever known, and I simply couldn't bear the thought of never seeing him again.

After a sleepless night spent muffling my misery in the bedclothes, I sneaked around to the back of Leonard's house just before setting off for school and tapped on the kitchen door. His mother opened it, and before she could express her surprise I thrust a note into her hands.

'Please give this to Leonard when you see him,' I said quickly.

'He's back,' she told me cheerfully, 'got back in the early hours. You can give it to him yourself!'

'No, I have to run or I'll be late for school!'

The day dragged on. I could barely sit through classes, but at long last school was over. I ran all the way to Dino's, and to my huge relief found Leonard waiting there for me. I slid into the booth opposite him.

'You got my note! Your mother's a marvel!' I said breathlessly. 'Did she tell you I met her yesterday? It's brilliant she's on our side!'

'Hey, slow down, will you! What's up?'

'Oh Leonard, my parents won't let me see you any more because you're not Jewish,' I blurted out miserably. 'They've forbidden me to see you or talk to you ever again and they really mean it. It's so unfair!'

I sat there, miserable and forlorn, my chin trembling and close to tears. Leonard leaned across the table, took my hand, and held it for the very first time and my heart beat faster. He looked at me long and hard, then letting my hand go he leaned back against the shiny padded seat.

'Okay, so…' as usual he paused, then chuckled, 'that's what *they* want. But how about you? What do *you* want?'

What did I want? How could he ask! 'I want to go on seeing you, of course!'

'Then that's what we'll do. We'll meet away from home… here, or wherever else we decide.'

'But how can we arrange it?' I asked agitatedly. 'I mean, we won't be able to talk to each other at home, and if they see me anywhere near you…'

Leonard grinned.

'Calm down and listen to me for a moment. There are a couple of loose bricks near the bottom of the wall between our back yards. I fixed one of them so I can take it out and store stuff behind it…'

'What stuff?'

'Never mind what stuff, just listen, will you? I'll loosen the brick behind mine on your side, and that way we can write notes and hide them there. If we're careful no one will notice. I'll fix it tonight and leave a twig sticking out on your side so you'll know which one it is.'

It seemed like a solution but I was apprehensive; truth to tell I didn't relish the idea of flouting my parents, my mother in particular; she was a strict authoritarian, and if thwarted she could be frightening.

'It sounds great,' I agreed, 'but what if…'

'What if nothing! Oh, come on, Elsa, cheer up. It'll be good fun!'

And in spite of my misgivings I knew that if I wanted to go on seeing Leonard, I had no alternative but to agree.

Leonard's plan seemed to work, and one day as we were sitting in the café catching up on news, Dino came over with our shakes, but instead of hurrying back to his post behind the bar as he usually did, he began wiping our spotless table vigorously with the cloth he always had tucked in the capacious pocket of his apron. We watched him bewildered. After a few moments he asked offhandedly, 'How's things?'

'Fine,' we both agreed.

'Good. That's-a nice.' He polished some more, then stepping back to admire his handiwork gave a sigh of satisfaction. 'That's-a better.' Then, just as he was about to turn and leave: 'By the way,' he said, trying to sound casual, 'when-a you both coming in before, you maybe noticed something different in the street right outside the door? Something… I dunno… something you not seen outside the door before?'

I thought for a moment and shook my head.

Dino decided to ignore me, and turned his attention to Leonard.

'Leonard, you like-a motor cars, no?'

'Certainly do!'

'And… 'scuse me askin', you know where I park-a my car every day?'

'Yup, right outside the café.'

'Then how come you don't notice in place where every day I'm-a parking my car, is today a different one?'

'I did notice,' Leonard told him, 'but I thought someone else had taken your space.'

'No, is not belong-a someone else, is belong-a me! Is-a mine! Is-a my own new car!' Dino crowed with delight. 'Is-a blue, is-a big, is-a beautiful, is-a mine!'

'Yours?' Leonard said, genuinely astonished. 'You mean that Chevy out there is yours?'

'That's-a right, Leonard my boy, is-a mine! Is-a my lovely, lovely blue Chevy! Tell-a me now, you like?'

'Absolutely!'

'You understand is not exactly new, but is-a nearly new, and is-a big now for my family. No more sitting on the top of each other.' Then, tucking the cloth back into his apron, he asked Leonard: 'You drive?'

'Yes I do,' came the reply.

'Well, one-a day maybe I let-a you to drive my lovely blue Chevy, huh? Maybe,' adding with a laugh as he walked away, 'or maybe no!'

'Leonard!' I said, surprised, 'I didn't know you could drive!'

He looked at me and chuckled.

'Ah, there's a lot you don't know about me, Elsa.'

'But you're only fifteen!' I continued. 'You don't have a licence!'

'Oh come on now, you don't need a licence to be able to drive. Anyone can drive. You could drive if you wanted to.'

'Could I? Really?' I was more than a little interested.

'Course you could. I'll teach you, if you like.'

'Right, you're on!'

And I put it out of my mind, along with all the other fanciful plans we had made.

There were three things that made my fourteenth birthday memorable. The first was that I actually drove a car for the first time. Well, perhaps 'drove' is an exaggeration… 'steered' would be more accurate. Leonard had left a note in our hiding place saying he had a birthday surprise for me and I was to meet him at Dino's after school. My mother had suggested I invite a few friends round to our house for what she called 'a little tea party', but seemed quite relieved when I declined her offer.

Leonard usually arrived at Dino's before me, but on this particular day there was no sign of him, and no, Dino hadn't seen him. I sat in the booth becoming more anxious as the minutes ticked by, and even Dino was getting a little edgy. Twenty minutes dragged by, by which time I had made my mind up that our secret was out and Leonard was being held hostage by my father, or else he'd been involved in a terrible accident and was lying in hospital, his life ebbing away.

'You want-a your shake now?' Dino had been watching me anxiously from behind his counter.

'No, I'll wait.'

'You want-a pastry?' he asked, nodding encouragement.

'No thanks, Dino.'

Just then a car pulled up outside, hooted loudly, and a minute later Leonard's redheaded friend Ian appeared at the café entrance.

'Elsa! Come on, move it!' he shouted, and promptly disappeared.

I grabbed my school hat and satchel and, running after him, saw him climb into the passenger seat of a dusty old pickup van. It was scarred and dented, its engine coughing and grinding, and the door that Ian held open was windowless. Behind the steering wheel sat Leonard, beaming.

'Get in quick!' he yelled over the racket. I piled in next to Ian, who sat scrunched uncomfortably between the two of us, the gearstick between his legs.

'Shut the door, Elsa!' Leonard yelled again, and after several unsuccessful slams the lock caught and we jolted away, soon picking up a surprising speed.

'Where did you get it?' I shouted, frantically hanging onto the windowless door frame.

'Found it!' came the reply.

'Where are we going?'

'Wait and see!' And whooping with pleasure, Leonard steered headlong into the oncoming traffic.

Ten minutes or so later he swerved onto a dirt road, bounced over several giant potholes, and slammed on the brakes, bringing the van to a rocking stop at the edge of an abandoned builders' yard strewn with buckled corrugated iron, worn-out tyres, and chunks of brick and old cement.

Leonard leaned across Ian and dangled the keys in front of me.

'All yours,' he said.

I looked at him uncomprehendingly.

'Don't tell me...' he paused, then came the chuckle, '...you've forgotten!'

'Forgotten what?'

'Good Heavens, girl! A couple of weeks ago?'

He waited, but I was none the wiser.

'Okay, listen to Leonard,' he instructed. 'A couple of weeks ago we were in Dino's, yes?'

'Yes,' I agreed, 'but then we're always in Dino's.'

'Yes,' he continued, 'but this time was different because Dino came over to our booth...'

'With our shakes, which he always does...'

'Will you shut it and let me finish, okay?' Leonard said in exasperation.

'Yeah,' Ian chipped in, 'shut it and let Lennie finish, okay?'

'Okay. Sorry.'

'Right. Dino came over with our shakes *as usual*... okay?' He glared at me, daring me to speak. 'Then he started polishing our table and talked about... talked about...'

'Oh, his car! His new car! Dino had just bought a new car!'

Leonard cheered. 'Hooray! We're getting somewhere. Now then, when he'd gone, what did we talk about?'

'His car?'

'Well, not exactly. Something to do with cars, though.'

I was trying hard to recall our conversation and failing miserably when Ian piped up.

'Come on, Lennie,' he said impatiently, 'for Gawd's sake tell her or we'll be here all day!'

'All right, then,' Leonard said, relenting, 'here's your clue! Happy birthday!' And with that he lobbed the car keys over to me. And then I remembered. Of course! This was to be my first driving lesson!

The fact that the vehicle was already in pretty bad shape helped, after all there wasn't much further damage I could do. However, when I climbed into the driver's seat I found I was too short to see over the steering wheel. We eventually reached a compromise which meant that Leonard sat in the driver's seat while I sat on his lap, my legs trapped between his, and we were off! We started tentatively with me steering carefully, while my gallant co-driver controlled the rest of whatever it took to keep the van moving. It wasn't long though before I got the hang of it, and we were gleefully throwing caution to the winds, risking life and limb. Leonard accelerated and braked while with ever growing confidence I turned the wheel hard, then let it spin back through my hands. The van pitched from side to side. Clouds of dust swirled as we zigged and zagged through the debris, sending bits and pieces flying. All the while Ian sat perched on a stack of worn tyres near the entrance, waving and cheering whenever we passed him. It was thrilling! We rattled and jolted around the yard until finally Leonard braked, and we skidded to a rocking standstill. Exhausted and exhilarated I tugged open the van door and dropped to the ground just as Ian came bounding towards us, whooping his pleasure. Standing beside me Leonard put a steadying hand on my shoulder.

'You, dear lady,' he drawled, 'have just qualified as an experienced and thoroughly professional co-driver of vans both old and older. I hereby wish you well, and all who drive with you.' And just when I thought things couldn't get any better, Leonard bent down and briefly brushed my cheek with his lips. That was the second memorable thing that happened that birthday.

The third thing was the gift of a large maroon leather-bound diary that a favourite aunt gave me.

'You really should keep a diary, you know,' she had said as she presented it to me, 'you'll be really pleased in later life that you did. I can't tell you how much I regret not having kept one myself when I was your age. So do try!'

In fact I was quite keen to get started. That night when my mother came in to say goodnight I was sitting in bed, pen in hand, deciding what to write in my very first entry.

'I'm delighted you're going to use Auntie May's lovely gift,' she said, taking the diary from me and turning it around in her hands. 'Mmm… I can smell the leather! It really is handsome, isn't it?'

'Yes, and I've decided I'm going to keep it here on my bedside table and write in it every night before I go to sleep.'

'Good idea,' my mother agreed. 'Have you started yet?'

'Not yet,' I told her, 'but it's going to be very private and personal, so you've got to promise me you'll never try to read it.'

'Of course not!' said my mother with an offended frown, 'I wouldn't dream of it!'

Since my parents' ultimatum, Leonard and I had become closer than ever, meeting whenever and wherever we could, and each night I poured my lovesick heart out onto the pages of my diary. Now the notes we left under the brick in the back wall were full of plans and secret thoughts. One morning I walked into the kitchen for breakfast before leaving for school, and as usual found my mother standing at the big iron stove waiting for the kettle to boil. I stepped out into the yard and wandered over to the wall, then making sure no one was watching, I pulled out the brick. Sure enough, there was Leonard's precious note and I hastily tucked it into the pocket of my cardigan. When I turned I found my mother standing at the back door, her face set as steel. There was nothing for it, and I walked slowly, reluctantly towards her, dreading what would happen next. As I reached her she held out her hand.

'Give it to me,' she said quietly. I felt sick with fright.

'Give it to me!' my mother repeated dangerously.

'What?' I managed, playing for time, although I knew the game was up, and denying it would only make her angrier.

'Oh for God's sake! That note in your pocket. It's no use pretending, Elsa, I know what's been going on.'

'Nothing's been going on,' I said, making matters worse.

'Oh, stop lying, Elsa, I'm not stupid,' she said furiously.

'I don't know what you mean!' I went, on digging myself deeper and deeper into a hole.

'Oh really? Well then let me tell you what I mean. I know exactly what you've been up to with that boy next door.'

I could barely breathe.

'And don't you dare continue with this ridiculous charade,' my mother's voice shook with rage, 'because I happen to know what's been going on behind my back. How dare you deliberately disobey me and your father? Don't you have any sense of shame?' And then it came, what I had dreaded even more than her temper.

'Give me the note!'

We stood looking at each other for a long moment.

'The note!' she repeated, her lips thin and tight. 'I know what's in it, Elsa. I've read your diary.'

I looked at her in disbelief, my mouth dry.

'My diary?' It came as a whisper. And suddenly I was angry, angry, not only with my mother, but with myself. How could I have been so stupid, so trusting! I should have known this might happen. Leaving my diary around had been naive, asking for trouble. And what would Leonard say? What would he think? I had betrayed him and now everything was spoilt.

'Come on!' she said, stretching a hand towards me, 'give me that note!'

I crushed the note in my pocket and held it tightly in my fist.

'No!'

It was the first time I had ever defied her. A look of fury crossed her face and she swung her arm but I stepped back and dodged the intended blow. We stood looking at one another, then my mother turned and strode back into the kitchen. She went over to the oven and picked up the iron lever used to lift the heavy hobs. Hooking it home she dragged one of the covers aside.

'In here.'

Reluctantly I took the screwed-up ball of paper from my pocket and dropped it onto the glowing coals, watching it catch at the edges, then curl and writhe into ash. My mother dragged the heavy cover back into place with a clang, and without looking at me left the room. Nothing had been said, but I think we both knew that what had just occurred had changed our relationship forever.

After school I waited at Dino's in case Leonard's note had suggested we should meet there, but he didn't show up. That evening I tried looking into his sitting room from my vantage point in the bathroom, but the curtains were drawn which meant his father was home, and in that case Leonard may well have disappeared for a few days to avoid him. The note would have told me. That night, hurt and humiliated, I shoved the offending diary under my bed, locked the door, and climbing into bed pulled the covers over my head, once again sobbing myself to sleep.

It was three days before Leonard reappeared. It had become almost routine for me to call in at Dino's on my way home after school to see if he was there, or whether he'd left a message for me. Dino was by now part of the conspiracy and was quite zealous in his role as go-between. This time, instead of shaking his head sympathetically, he nodded his head vigorously and, beaming, waved me into our usual booth where Leonard sat, casual and smiling. As I slid into the seat opposite him I noticed he wasn't wearing his school uniform.

'Oh, it's so good to see you!' I said, breathless with relief. 'Where…' Suddenly I remembered his mother's distant warning about keeping his movements to himself, and managed a rather lame switch. 'Where's your school uniform?'

Leonard didn't answer. Instead, maddeningly, he just kept smiling that characteristic smile of his. I held back my frustration and with a superhuman effort waited for some sort of explanation about this recent escapade. He studied me for what seemed an age, then looking around carefully, leaned over the table towards me and slowly pulled a wad of notes out of the inside pocket of his duffle coat, shielding it with his hands.

'Look,' he said quietly, 'one hundred quid!'

I had never seen so much money before!

'Where did you get it?' I asked, wide-eyed.

'I earned it!' He slipped the money back into his coat and beckoned me to come closer.

'I'll tell you, but you must swear this is a secret strictly between the two of us. Okay?'

I nodded, scarcely able to breathe. Leonard paused and chuckled.

'Quite a while ago I decided I had to make enough money to get away from here, to get away from that man.'

He had been talking quietly. Now he stopped, and I waited.

'I was lucky,' he continued. 'I put out feelers and got to hear about some people who… deal with cars. Well, they took me on. That's why I sometimes stay out late, or disappear for a while.'

'What do you mean, took you on? What do you do?'

'I help respray them and change the number plates.'

'Stolen cars?' I was shocked.

'Shush!' He looked around sharply, then went on: 'Only some of them are actually stolen. The rest are sort of… found!' And he chuckled.

'Leonard, you're crazy! It's dangerous!' I hissed angrily. 'What if you get caught?'

'I won't get caught!' he said vehemently. 'For a start, no one there knows who I am or where to find me. Anyway, they couldn't care less as long as I do my job and keep my lip buttoned. As for the cars, by the time we've finished with them there's absolutely no way they could be traced!'

My heart was thumping in my chest, yet although I felt scared for him, part of me found it thrilling.

'Does your mother know?'

'Of course not!' he gave a short laugh. 'She suspects there must be something dodgy about what I do when I give her money... she's not stupid. But she needs the extra cash... he's a mean old sod. She trusts me to look after myself, and I do.'

I sat looking at him, apprehensive of what was to come.

'The thing is, I'm planning to leave... I've been planning it for a long while now. I'm going to hitchhike from Jo'burg to Cape Town, then get on a ship sailing to England. I'll get a job in London, any job, but hopefully with prospects, and once I've saved up enough, I'm going to send for my mother to join me.'

'But how will you pay your fare? And how will you manage until you do get a job?' I asked, trying to keep my voice steady.

'I told you... I've been saving for a long while now, and getting paid pretty well,' he told me, adding with a chuckle, 'not only for what I've been doing, but for keeping my mouth shut as well!'

My throat hurt from holding back the sobs. I couldn't bear the thought of him going away and leaving me alone.

'When...' I managed and hesitated, not wanting to hear the answer, 'when... do you think you'll go?'

'Pretty soon,' he said, avoiding my eyes.

I dared not speak, knowing that if I did it would start an avalanche of tears that once released would never stop. Leonard reached over and took both my hands in his, and so we sat in our favourite booth in Dino's, saying nothing, just looking down at our hands clasped together.

The sound of gravel being thrown against my bedroom window woke me. It was midnight and, bleary-eyed, I struggled out of bed and peered through the slats of the blinds. Leonard was sitting astride the wall between the two houses, his school scarf wound high around his neck. He gestured at me to open the window.

'I'm off,' he said in a low voice. 'A car is picking me up at the bottom of the road. I'm getting a lift to Bloemfontein, then I'll hitch to the Cape.'

'Well…' My thoughts were in a whirl… I couldn't think of what to say. 'Well, you be careful, look after yourself, don't go mad!' I tried to sound jokey, and hoped the dark would hide my misery.

'Don't worry, Elsa.' I waited for the chuckle. It came. 'I will.'

I held my breath, hoping he would say something… anything that I could remember and hold close until the pain of parting grew less. Instead he grasped the wall and prepared to slip down on the other side.

'Got to go. You be good. And…' the pause, the chuckle, 'be nice to my mother, she's going to miss me.'

He dropped from view, but a moment later his head reappeared.

'And Elsa… make sure you miss me too!'

Then he was gone.

Now and again his mother kept me informed about what Leonard was up to. She told me that shortly after his hurried midnight farewell he had managed to get a job as a kitchen hand on a Union Castle ship heading for Southampton; and, a while later, that he was in London odd-jobbing and deciding what line of work to pursue. As time went by I became occupied with other interests and Leonard slowly faded, at first out of my life, and then out of my memory. It would be another three years before we would meet again.

I was seventeen years old and half way through a university degree, when my burning ambition for a future as an actress overcame my less pressing need to get a degree in Fine Arts. After an extended battle with my parents they eventually called a truce and agreed, for the sake of sanity, to let me audition for a place at the Royal Academy of Dramatic Art in London. My mother accompanied me and my large metal trunk of belongings across the ocean to Southampton, and thence by train to the capital city. I managed to fail the audition, but they did offer me a three-month interim term at their preparatory school, after which, I was told, I could reapply. It had a students' hostel attached, and my mother, more than somewhat relieved, saw me safely deposited within its supervised walls, and fled back to her warmer comfort zone.

One evening a few weeks later, a fellow student put her head around the door of my room just as I was settling down to learn a poem for the next day's verse speaking class.

'Phone call for you.'

'It can't be for me,' I said without looking up, 'no one knows I'm here.'

'Well, they asked for you,' the messenger said tartly. 'The receiver's off the hook and I'm not going back down to replace it,' and she disappeared. There was a coin-box telephone on the first floor landing which students used but I hadn't given the number to anyone, including my parents. I trudged down the stairs impatient to get back to my memorising and was about to put the swinging receiver back onto its cradle when curiosity got the better of me.

'Hello, who is that?' I asked irritably.

'Who do you think, Elsa?'

It was Leonard's unmistakeable drawl!

'Leonard! Is that you?'

'Who else?' He chuckled his distinctive little chuckle, sending a remembered thrill through me.

'Good Heavens! Where are you?'

'Here, in London.'

'Wonderful! But how on earth did you find me?' I asked breathlessly.

'I'll tell you when I see you. When can we meet and where? I'm working at the Savoy Hotel, but I can get time off.'

'It'll have to be the weekend; the matron doesn't approve of us going out in the evenings.'

'Matron? I thought you were studying acting, not medicine!'

'It's a hostel, idiot! How about Saturday morning?'

'Perfect. Where?' he asked.

'Do you know Highgate?'

'I'll find it.'

'There's a nice little Italian coffee house on the High Street,' I told him. 'It's called La Giaconda. We could meet there at, say, eleven?'

'See you there at eleven.'

When I arrived Leonard was already there, waiting for me. He had chosen a corner table from which he could see the door, and by the time I had searched him out he was standing, arms outstretched, and smiling that smile. I weaved my way through the busy café, and laughing with pleasure threw my arms around him. We rocked back and forth, holding one another close. It felt wonderful. I reached up to run my fingers through his curly blonde hair... something I had always longed to do... and found it unexpectedly stubborn and wiry. For a split second a feeling of surprise and disappointment overcame me, but I shook it off. How ridiculous! Leonard was here, and at last there was no one around to stop us from being together. Reluctantly I had to admit that I was lonely. Since my arrival at the school I had made no particular friends, and it would be great to have someone around to confide in. Now we sat smiling stupidly at one another, saying nothing. I decided he hadn't changed much in the passing three years, but then Leonard had always looked older than his age. Now, relaxed and confident, there was a worldly air about him that made me feel a little unnerved, and seemed to put an edge of distance between us. At last he broke the silence.

'So...' he paused his inevitable pause, then chuckled as I knew he would, 'so, you're going to be a "star" are you?' He smiled at me quizzically. To my dismay the way he said it sounded as though he were indulging a child and put me on the defensive.

'What I'm going to be, Leonard, is an actress, and hopefully a successful one,' I said tartly, and immediately felt guilty. We had only just found each other and here I was letting my insecurities get the better of me.

'I don't doubt it!' he said with genuine warmth, making me feel even worse. But my blissful mood had been bruised, and I had to make an effort not to show it.

'Leonard,' I said a little too brightly, 'before we go any further you must tell me how on earth you managed to find me here!'

'You won't believe it, but it was through my dear old ma back in Jo'burg,' he drawled, pausing before he continued. 'She managed to winkle out details of where you were and what you were doing from your very own mother!'

'My mother speaking to your mother?' I was flabbergasted. 'You're kidding me!'

'No, I swear it's true. They keep up a front of neighbourliness for appearances' sake and, when it can't be avoided, they have the odd polite, strained conversations.'

'How pathetic! Still, I'm amazed my mother tells your mother about me!'

Leonard laughed. 'Listen, your mother is so proud of you she'd give your full and detailed particulars to any passing stranger who expressed the slightest interest in your progress up the ladder of success!'

'Oh dear, poor mum. She's always complained that when I do anything my parents are proud of, my father takes all the credit. She'd say: "I keep reminding him that I happen to be your parent too!"'

It was true. I knew she was supportive and proud of me, and it would have come as no surprise if she'd confessed to actually looking forward to those 'strained conversations'. Suddenly I felt an enormous sense of guilt about my often discordant relationship with my mother. I needed to change the subject.

'And you, Leonard, tell me what's been happening to you?'

He settled back into his chair and began. He had crossed from Cape Town to Southampton working his passage as a kitchen hand on board ship. He found the catering service to his liking and decided to pursue it as a possible future career. Arriving in London he silver-tongued his way into a training course at the Savoy Hotel (no surprise to me!), starting on the bottom rung, with the guarantee of a higher position within the hotel group if he proved his potential. Now, three years later, he had just signed a contract for his very first managerial post.

'That's wonderful! Congratulations!' I said, reaching out to take his hand, but to my hurt surprise he pulled his hand away.

'No, wait! Sorry,' he said apologetically, 'this is too important.'

I waited, and after a short pause he went on. 'I've always saved as much as I could, putting it into a building society account that I never touched. It's for… well, it *was* for my mother, to get her over here and give her a sort of allowance. Not much, you understand, but just so that she could be independent, although to start with she'd live with me.' He paused again and then laughed a short, bitter laugh. 'I called it Betty's Saving. Not savings, you understand, but Saving.' He laughed again.

'I love that!'

'Thanks. I thought she would too, but… well, a month ago I decided that finally, finally I had enough saved to send for her…' He stopped again, then said so quietly I could barely hear him over the café hubbub, 'It never occurred to me that it might not be what she wanted! What a fool! I was chasing my own dream without considering what she might want.'

'Oh Leonard! You mean...' He cut me off before I could finish.

'She declined my offer.' He spoke the words loudly, quickly, and looked away.

'But why?' I instantly regretted the question, knowing there was nothing I could do or say that would help.

'She pleaded a reluctance not only to travel, but to leave the sunnier climes of the land of her birth for the less reliable climate of the UK.' He shook his head, then looked at me with a wry smile. 'I still find it hard to get my head around the fact that she didn't jump at the chance to get away from that man, that bloody man. But that's life.'

'Maybe she'll change her mind,' I offered lamely.

'Nice try, but I know she won't. In spite of all my attempts at persuasion, she remains intransigent. And over there.'

He leaned forward and grasped my hand.

'Funny, isn't it? You're the only person I could tell, the only person I know who would understand how I feel. She definitely won't change her mind, that much I know. And of course I'm desperately disappointed. Desperately.' He paused again, then releasing my hand he leaned back and went on: 'I've got used to the idea now... more or less... and thinking about it, well, that means I'm free from any obligations. And what's more, I have a little nest egg to draw on!'

I looked at him uncomprehendingly.

'Don't you see? I'm free! Free to do whatever I like!'

'And that would be... what?'

'Oh listen Elsa, I've thought about it really carefully.'

I nodded, wondering what was coming next.

'To begin with, I'm going to tear up the contract I signed with the hotel syndicate.'

'Tear it up?' I was shocked. 'But you can't do that, can you? I mean, isn't a contract, well, a contract?'

'Yes it is, but the thing is, even though I've signed on the dotted line they can't stop me leaving. The worst they can do is refuse to give me any references. Anyway, I'm going to tell them tomorrow. They won't be pleased!' he chuckled. 'In fact they'll probably tell me to walk straight away!'

Now I was totally confused.

'Surely without references you won't be able to get another job... well, certainly not in the catering business?'

'Maybe not here, not in this country, but I'm not planning to stay. I'm off to the U S of A. America, that's the place for me! Broader horizons, richer pickings, and everyone there open to ideas for making money! Well, Elsa, I've got ideas, and now I've got enough money to give it a go!'

I had never seen Leonard so excited, so animated. It was clear nothing was going to stop him.

'So, the land of opportunity calls,' I said, smiling warmly at him. 'I truly hope it works out for you. I'm sure it will. When are you planning to go?'

His answer didn't surprise me.

'The day after tomorrow.'


When I answered the phone in the hallway outside my bedsit, the last thing I expected to hear was Leonard's instantly recognisable voice; I was surprised and delighted. Once again he had discovered my whereabouts through his mother.

'I've just been over to Jo'burg to see her,' he told me, 'and I decided to stop off in London and catch up with a few friends from the Savoy... and you, of course.'

It had been two and a half years since our encounter in Highgate. I was living in digs in South Kensington and, as most struggling young actors do whilst hanging around for the next possible casting, taking any odd job that turned up. At the time I was working as a hostess cum waitress, serving drinks and curries in a small club in Soho not far from the local dole office. The club was frequented mainly by actors who would drop in after signing on, and soon after starting the job I had met and fallen in love with one of them.

Leonard and I arranged to meet the following afternoon in Kensington Gardens. It was one of those warm, breezy late summer afternoons, and for a while we sat on the grass in the shade of a tall tree without speaking much. Young lovers, absorbed and oblivious, strolled by arm in arm, and pensioners sat cradled in canvas deckchairs, half asleep in the sun. Leonard had put on a little weight but it suited him. I noticed again the slight curving of his little fingers that I used to find so endearing, and wondered now if it might be a sign of impending arthritis. But although the frisson I used to feel whenever I'd been with him had evaporated, he was still the charmer I remembered with affection. After a while he lay back, his arms pillowing his head, and began filling in the gap since last we'd met.

Pausing and chuckling, he told me that when he'd first arrived in the States he had decided California was the place for him. He moved into Santa Monica, and soon found a job in a local hotel owned by a syndicate. From modest beginnings he was soon managing one of their motels along the coast, and now, he said, he was overseeing several other of their properties.

'I'm impressed,' I told him, 'but I'm not remotely surprised.'

'Why, thank you, dear lady!' he responded. 'And how about you? What's been happening? How's your career coming along? Are you a star yet?'

His question, accompanied by that wry smile of his, triggered a sudden recollection of our conversation all those years ago in Highgate when he had seemed to trivialise my ambition to succeed. I tried to shake it off but it seems old wounds can still smart, and it took an effort of will to sound amiable as I tried to explain how precarious and overcrowded my chosen career was proving to be, and how daunting the competition.

'Anyway, I have a temporary job at the moment... at least I hope it's temporary, just to keep the pennies rolling in. I'm a waitress, only they've given me the grander title of "hostess". And before you jump to any conclusions, I really am just a glorified waitress, no more than that. But I'm enjoying it and I'm meeting a lot of really nice people. Mostly actors.'

'Socialising with The Enemy, eh?' The pause, the chuckle. 'Could prove useful, no?'

'Hardly!' I laughed. 'Most of them are on the hunt for work too. Well, when I say most, there are one or two who are doing pretty well. As a matter of fact...'

I wasn't sure how to continue.

'Yes?' Leonard was watching me carefully.

'In fact... while I've been there I've got to know one of them quite well.'

I looked away, knowing I was blushing and hating myself for it.

'Really? And how well is "quite well"?'

'Oh come on, Leonard,' I said with an embarrassed laugh, 'you know what I mean!'

'Do you mean you know him very quite well, or quite very well? There is a difference, you know.'

'Leonard, stop it. If you want to know, we're planning to move in together.'

It took a moment before he responded.

'That's serious stuff! Lucky man! An actor, eh? Not the most emotionally stable people in the world, actors! Come to think of it, not the most financially stable either!'

'What are you talking about? Honestly, Leonard, how can you say those things when you haven't even met him? As a matter of fact,' my temper was rising, 'he's one of the most sincere people I have ever met. And it just so happens that he's regarded as a very fine actor with a great future ahead of him. London isn't Los Angeles, you know! From what I hear almost everyone in LA, no matter how untalented, is chasing a career in show business. Everyone! Petrol pump attendants, shop assistants, bank clerks, probably every single waitress is an aspiring…'

I stopped in midstream.

'Oh Christ.'

'What?'

'That's me. I'm a waitress. And I'm aspiring.'

'True, but…'

'No, Leonard, don't you see? Here I am yelling at you for… I don't know… stereotyping actors, and I'm doing exactly the same thing! I mean, how pathetic, how ridiculous is that?'

He thought for a minute.

'I'll go for pretty ridiculous!' he offered.

'There's nothing pretty about it,' I said miserably.

'Okay then,' he paused and chuckled, 'how about plain ridiculous?'

We erupted into laughter.

'Look, I'm really sorry, I didn't mean to upset you,' he said apologetically. 'It's just that I really do care about you, and I care what happens to you.'

'I know you do, Lennie.'

'I'll stop playing devil's advocate. All that really matters is that he makes you happy.'

We sat quietly for a while, and when he next spoke Leonard sounded suddenly serious.

'So tell me, are you absolutely sure you love him?'

'Absolutely sure.'

'And what about him? Does he love you?'

I smiled. 'Yes, I think so.'

'And will he take care of you?'

'I think so.'

'And will you marry him and live happily ever after?' He smiled his lopsided smile.

'Possibly!'

'Well,' he said after a pause, ' that seems to be that, then.'

His next question surprised me.

'And what about your career?' he asked.

'What about it?'

'Will you give it up?'

I looked at him in surprise. It was a possibility that had never crossed my mind.

'Good Lord, no! Absolutely not!' I laughed derisively at the implausibility of such a notion.

'And what if that's what he wants you to do?'

'Don't be ridiculous, Leonard, he would never ask me to give it up. He just wouldn't!' The words came out more strongly than I intended.

'All right, take it easy, I'm only asking!'

'I'm sorry. I didn't mean to snap. It's just that…'

'I know.'

The day was fading and the breeze had dropped. Leonard lay back on the grass and closed his eyes and I watched him, thinking how far we had journeyed since that night when he'd thrown stones against my bedroom window, and remembering how bereft I had felt.

'I've been married,' he said suddenly, his eyes still closed.

'You?'

'Yup. Married and divorced within five months. Big mistake. Ill… judged.' He lingered over the last two words as though he were testing them. He told me his marriage had been a spur of the moment decision after a brief and torrid affair with a young American air hostess he'd met on one of his regular internal flights. Once things between them had cooled down, the only thing they had managed to agree on was a swift divorce.

'It's not something I particularly care to dwell on,' he told me, opening his eyes and sitting up. 'Still, I suppose with luck we live and learn.'

'How miserable for you Lennie, I'm so sorry. Better luck next time, eh?'

He laughed.

'As a matter of fact I have a confession to make. Now… promise not to laugh.'

'All right, I promise,' I said apprehensively.

'Well, believe it or not I was going to ask if you would come back to the States with me... no, please don't say anything. Of course deep down I knew it would be pretty unlikely, but... well, no harm in wondering if... Anyway, I kind of knew it wasn't going to happen.'

I was literally speechless! It was the last thing I could have anticipated.

'Oh Leonard...'

'No, let me finish. A few months ago I met someone who works in one of the motels I manage in Florida. She's a receptionist. Not what you'd call beautiful, but very attractive. As a matter of fact she reminds me a lot of you.'

'I'll take that as a compliment!' I said, not sure I meant it.

'And she's nice. Very nice, and we get on really well.' It was his turn now to seem embarrassed. 'Anyway, to cut a long story short, she tells me she loves me.'

'And does she?'

He smiled. 'Yes, I think so.'

'And do you love her?'

'I think so.'

'Then will you marry her and live happily ever after?'

'Possibly.'

And he smiled his lopsided smile. But it didn't quite reach his eyes.


By the time we next met my private life was in pieces. I had been through a difficult marriage (it seems Leonard may have had a point about the acting profession!), a miserable divorce, and a doomed love affair. Fortunately my career and my sense of humour were still intact.

I was rehearsing an episode of a television series in a church hall near the Oval, when the production assistant came in from her office and crossed to where I was sitting.

'There's a phone call for you,' she said. 'He wouldn't give me his name, says it's a surprise. Actually we had quite a chat.

Apparently he phoned Equity to get your agent's number and she told him you were rehearsing here. I was really surprised! Agents are usually pretty cagey. Mind you, if he chatted her up the way he did me…! He has a really sexy voice and an odd little laugh…'

But long before she'd finished speaking I knew it was Leonard.

I picked him up at Waterloo station that evening on my way home. He was easily recognisable, although his blonde, curly hair was bleached almost white from the Californian sun. He wore a pair of faded blue denim dungarees over a sleeveless white T-shirt, and as he slung his large duffle bag onto the back seat I noticed he was wearing the sort of strappy buckled sandals I have always associated with children. This wasn't quite the sophisticated thirty-something possible lover I had anticipated! But then, as we drove through London, the old magic began to work its charm, and by the time we reached my small suburban house I was a little breathless with excitement and anticipation. Would Leonard and I, after all these years, finally become lovers? Would he turn out to be the answer to my search for a long-term, stable relationship?

That evening over a hastily prepared alfresco meal washed down with a bottle of reasonably good wine, we brought each other more or less up to date. I recounted briefly what I had been up to since we'd last met many moons ago in Kensington Gardens, and reminded him of the receptionist he'd intended to marry. No, he told me, they hadn't married, but had lived together for a few years until it became clear their relationship was souring and they had agreed to part. Soon after, he'd met and married a journalist who turned out to be insecure and neurotic. Apparently she had spent their short time together discussing him in analytical detail with her female editor who eventually advised her to leave him on the grounds that she was losing her sanity… though he wasn't sure whether it was the editor's or the wife's sanity that was at risk! Meanwhile his career had taken him further up the ladder, and he was now considering buying and running a motel of his own. When I asked after his mother, he told me he had continued to try to persuade her to change her mind but she had remained intransigent, and four years ago she had died of a heart attack. As for his father, Leonard didn't know where he was or even if he was still alive, and neither did he care.

He stayed for a week, and after the first exciting night of long-awaited fulfilment we settled into a pleasant routine. I rehearsed during the day, and each evening looked forward to the novel experience of returning to his welcoming embraces and kisses. With no one else to consider, we made love whenever and wherever the urge took us, from a slow and leisurely coupling on the cool grass under a star-sprinkled sky, to an uncomfortable sandwiching in my narrow porcelain bath tub; and all the while I wondered wickedly what my mother would have made of it all!

However, as the week progressed, to my guilty shame I found that certain of Leonard's mannerisms began to irritate me. The drawling speech I had found so beguiling began to make me grit my teeth, his sentences stretching beyond patience. And as for the chuckle that peppered his speech, it now seemed a thoroughly unnecessary affectation; but then he would look at me and smile his lopsided smile, and all would be forgiven. Well, almost.

At first I had managed to ignore the anomalous denim dungarees worn constantly along with the chunky children's sandals, but I was forced to face reality when a friend returning a borrowed CD met him briefly at the front door. She phoned me later and, barely hiding her amusement, asked: 'Where on earth did you find Beach Boy?' I didn't know who I was angrier with, my friend for making the observation, or me for having to accept that there was no doubt about it… the epithet fitted perfectly. In spite of that setback, we were still enjoying our time together. We seemed to have run out of conversation but the silences were comfortable, as was the sex.

One evening towards the end of the week we were enjoying an aperitif as we watched the news on TV, when Leonard mentioned that he'd promised to visit some relatives of a friend of his whilst he was in England. He took a piece of paper from his pocket.

'They live in Devon. Would you mind if I gave them a call?'

'Of course not!' I told him, 'you don't have to ask. Go ahead.'

'Thanks.' I reached for the remote control.

'No, no need to turn the sound down,' he said, getting out of his chair, 'I'll use the phone in the bedroom.'

A short while later he was back.

'Well, that's a duty done!' he said brightly, throwing himself onto the sofa beside me and putting an arm around my shoulder. 'I told them to expect me the day after tomorrow. Is that okay with you? I mean, I can easily arrange to stay with you a bit longer if you'd like me to.' He spoke softly, nuzzling my ear: 'Although you know what they say... leave them wanting more...'

'No, no, that's absolutely fine,' I replied, and hoped I didn't sound too enthusiastic.

At first I missed having someone to come back to at the end of the day as well as having someone around to discuss things with, however trivial; but, I told myself, you're a loner, you enjoy your own company, and in a few days I had picked up the threads of the social life I'd neglected whilst he'd been staying. However, I was surprised and rather hurt that he hadn't called me as he'd promised, if only to thank me for board, not to mention bed. He hadn't left me a contact number or address, and at the time I hadn't particularly wanted him to. Now I regretted it, and by the end of the week, true to form I began wishing I'd asked him to stay on, wondering why on earth I had let this golden opportunity pass me by. I fretted and mooched about the house, reluctant to go out in case I missed the phone call I now desperately wanted him to make.

One day, fed up with myself, I decided to set about cleaning the house from top to bottom. I began in the bedroom, furiously vacuuming places the vacuum cleaner had never vacuumed before. As I shoved the bedside table to one side, the telephone slipped off, and bending down to retrieve it I noticed a slip of paper on the carpet near the skirting board. I fished it out and found a phone number written on it along with the name Cookson. It was Leonard's writing, and was almost certainly the Devon number Leonard had called before he left.

A pleasant-sounding woman answered. Yes, she told me, she was Mrs Cookson. No, she was sorry, but Leonard wasn't there, he had left for California a few days earlier. No, she didn't have a contact number for him but she'd be happy to give me her niece's, where I would be bound to reach him. She told me how disappointed she was she wouldn't be fit enough to travel to Florida for their wedding, and her only worry was that her niece might not enjoy living in a motel in such a remote location. Still, she was sure being the wife of the manager would make all the difference. She was very glad to have met him, and wasn't he a nice young man!

# JACK AND MOLLY

It was the first time I had actually seen my name up in lights. Admittedly not above the title nor directly underneath it, but for alphabetical reasons, I told myself, third down the list. Still, there it was: SHEILA STEAFEL! Each evening on my way to the theatre I would emerge from Leicester Square tube station, dodge the cars as I crossed St Martin's Lane, and try to avoid looking across the street until I reached the little Italian restaurant opposite the theatre. Then I'd stop, turn, and marvel at the sight of my name spelled out in neon. It never failed to thrill, or indeed, surprise me. It had been a long haul, but it seemed now at last, here in my mid forties, I had finally made it.

As it happened, that year we had the hottest summer anyone could remember, and it was clear that only dedicated theatregoers would willingly pay to sit and sweat in a darkened auditorium to watch a cast of indifferent singers accompanied by a honky-tonk piano perform an entertainment that would have made *The Magic Roundabout* seem challenging. Resurrected from the past when its naive simplicity had made it a sell-out success, the current critics, worn out by sophistication and imponderables, had given our production their seal of approval. But in spite of this the houses were meagre, and the weather forecasts indicated no change. The ancient electric fan loaned to me by the stage manager simply stirred the humid dressing room air, and attempts to apply makeup to a face running with perspiration were useless. I would cover my face with a tissue, pat the sweat away, and try to apply foundation, but it was like trying to make oil stay put on a non-stick frying pan. Eye makeup ran, and eventually I decided I would have to appear without the enhancement of war paint.

One midweek matinee, just as I was about to slip off my thin cotton dressing gown and climb reluctantly into the thick tweed suit I wore in the first act, I remembered the note lying on my dressing table that the stage doorman had handed me.

*Dear Miss Steafel,* it read, *I hope you won't mind us writing to you, but we are in this afternoon, seeing your performance for the third time. We've been huge fans of yours ever since we saw you being brilliant in the TV series* How's Your Father *and we've followed your career ever since. We're so delighted you've finally got your name up in lights, though of course we both think you should be above the title, but at least it's a step in the right direction.*

I must confess I felt a growing warmth towards this couple, and read on.

*We've never written a 'fan' letter before, and we're not sure whether this is asking too much, but would you consider letting us come round after the show this afternoon, just for a couple of minutes? We promise not to outstay our welcome, and if we do, you have our permission to say so and we'll disappear!*

*With thanks for all the pleasure you've given us over the years and all good wishes for your future success.*

*Molly and Jack Edwards*

*P.S. We have a small gift for you, which we will leave at the stage door if you would rather not see us.*

It was so delightfully and honestly written that I decided no harm could be done by a brief meeting, and a few minutes later when my dresser came in I told her to let the stage doorman know he could let the couple who had left the note come through to my dressing room after the show.

Molly and Jack turned out to be middle-aged, amusing, and down to earth. She was plump and of a sunny disposition, he rather serious and a little reserved. They knew as much if not more about my career than I could remember, and as good as their word, they disappeared almost as soon as I had started to suggest I thought it time I got ready for the evening show. As they left they presented me with a box of the most expensive chocolates, as well as a bottle of excellent vintage wine. There was a note attached signed by Jack, and it read: *Indulge yourself... you could do with a lot more flesh on those talented bones!* Truth to tell I thought it a touch too personal, but the gifts were so generous that I felt I ought at least to write them a note of thanks. There was a rather elaborately printed address on their notepaper, and I sent them a brief thank you for their gifts and thought no more about it. I should have realised, of course, that they were bound to respond, and once again it seemed churlish not to reply; and so it went, until a more-or-less regular correspondence was passing between us.

I was beginning to regard them as, for want of a better description, 'friendly acquaintances', and when they wrote to say they were coming yet again to see the show and invited me to dine with them afterwards in a nearby restaurant, in spite of slight misgivings I accepted. Throughout the dinner it was clear Molly doted on her husband, never taking her eyes off him and laughing a little too much at his dry observations. Jack became quite expansive, telling me of his long employment with a well known wine importer in the city. Molly was an assessor in an insurance company, and they had lived for many years in the same small suburban house with few overheads. This meant that although not exactly wealthy, they could indulge their two extravagances: collecting rare porcelain ornaments, and seeing every musical show in the West End, often several times over. The venue they favoured most was the Theatre Royal in Drury Lane. They were drawn to its grandeur, the plush comfort of the foyers and bars, the opulent auditorium, but mostly it was the atmosphere that captured their imaginations.

'Sometimes when we go there, if it's a show we know very well, after the interval, we'll just sit in the circle bar sipping our drinks and listening to the music,' said Molly. 'It's very faint, of course, but we can still hear it.'

'And she sings along!' said Jack with a laugh.

'I do, I sing along. Quietly, of course! The bar staff used to look at us as if we were mad, but they've got quite used to us now.'

All in all I enjoyed my evening with them, except for the remark Jack made as he helped me into my coat.

'You really should plump up a bit, Sheila. Men like something they can get hold of, and it's not healthy to be so skinny! You need someone to take you in hand!'

I could feel my gorge rise. Who did he think he was making such personal remarks? Before I could respond Molly put a hand on Jack's shoulder.

'Jack, don't be so personal!' she admonished with a smile. 'Sheila's in great shape and I'm sure she's happy with things just the way they are.' Then, turning to me: 'Take no notice of him,' she said, 'it's just his way of saying he cares about you. Sometimes it can sound a bit too personal, I know, but his heart's in the right place.' She spoke so earnestly I decided to take it at face value and put it out of my mind.

I felt I ought to reciprocate the meal, and decided that instead of taking them out to an equivalently expensive restaurant, I would invite them to my house for a traditional Sunday lunch. In order to ease any awkwardness I also invited along a young couple, friends of long standing. The mix was a good one and the lunch went well. As we sat over coffee, Jack asked if he could see the garden. Winter was just around the corner and there wasn't much to admire; the roses were lank and overgrown, the shrubs wild and in need of attention, and the lawn was marked with muddy tracks where the dogs had chased off marauding squirrels.

'Are you sure?' I asked, trying to hide my reluctance. 'It's a bit chilly out there.'

'Oh, Jack doesn't feel the cold!' said Molly.

'I daresay Sheila does, though,' Jack said with a grin, 'just look at her…'

But before he could finish Molly interrupted with a warning 'Jack!'

I fetched a coat from the hall cupboard and Jack followed me outside through the conservatory door.

'I'm afraid it's a bit of a mess at the moment,' I told him. 'You'll have to wait until spring when the garden's had a bit of T.L.C.'

'Actually, that was what I wanted to talk to you about.'

'What? Spring?'

'No, no. It's about…' Jack was floundering. 'Look, I'm sorry to drag you outside like this, but I wanted a word.' He stopped and I waited with some trepidation. 'I wanted to apologise for saying what I did the evening we took you to dinner.'

'Oh there's no need…' I began, but he held up a hand.

'Please, let me finish. You see, Molly and I have been great admirers of you and your work ever since we first saw you on television, and when we actually met you in your dressing room, the last thing we expected was that we'd become your friends. In fact at one point we did wonder whether perhaps we'd foisted ourselves on you.'

'Oh Jack, of course not!' I said a little too enthusiastically.

Perhaps they had, but if so, did it matter? Did I think of them as friends? Did I want them as friends? After all we had little in common, apart from a liking for good wine and an interest in theatre.

'But here we are having lunch with you in your home,' Jack continued, 'and we've met some of your friends, so perhaps now we can really call ourselves your friends. And I can't tell you how much that means to us!'

I was too embarrassed to offer any response, but instead gave a weak, meaningless smile.

'And whatever happens, whenever you need us, we'll be there for you. I intend to watch over you!' And, putting a proprietary hand on my shoulder, he began steering me towards the house. 'Now then, we'd better get you in,' he continued, 'you're shivering! You must be feeling the cold!'

But it wasn't only the cold that made me shiver.

Nonetheless I felt I couldn't just drop them, particularly after Jack's declaration of loyalty, and a pleasant enough cordiality ensued by post. I confess I found it flattering to have such devoted followers even though I felt guilty, admitting to myself they were not my sort of people. Molly wrote more and more often, and soon I was receiving long missives regaling me with details of shopping sprees, theatre visits, and gossip about her colleagues at work, little of which interested me. At first I replied politely enough and then tried to curb the flow by not responding. But it made no difference; still the letters came. From time to time there would be an elegantly boxed bottle of wine waiting for me at the stage door, always with a note from Jack, and always, much to my irritation, containing some cryptic remark or other regarding my lack of avoirdupois. But most unsettling was the added reminder that even though I may not have been aware of it, he would always be there for me.

A few months later the run of the play ended, and, as is the way of it, the management gave a last-night party for the company and all those involved. They had taken over a reception room in a nearby hotel, allowing two guests per person, and I decided it would be an ideal opportunity to repay the Edwards' loyalty. Naturally they were delighted, and I arranged to meet after the show in the hotel foyer. I could scarcely believe my eyes when I saw that Molly was wearing an exact replica of the dress I had worn in the final act of the play! Exact but for the size, and the resulting travesty did her no favours. Before I was able to speak she threw her arms around me, bursting with excitement.

'This was Jack's idea! We decided it would be a lovely surprise for you, After all, imitation is the sincerest form of flattery! And you've no idea how many people have stopped and asked me about it! Now I know how it feels to be you!'

What followed was one of the most embarrassing evenings I can remember. The next morning I determined to break off my association with the Edwards as swiftly as I could. But how? How could I extricate myself from this ridiculous situation without appearing hurtful and callous? Then the doorbell rang, and provided the answer in the shape of an elaborate hamper from Fortnum's; it goes without saying that it was from Jack and Molly. I sent them a brief note in which I said I could no longer accept gifts from them, that I would be donating this latest offering to an old-age home, and that any future gifts would similarly be dealt with. I heard nothing from them, and began to allow myself a sense of relief.

I had invited a few friends round to dinner one evening, and after the meal as we sat in the living room chatting, the doorbell rang. It was quite late and I am rather nervous about unexpected callers, so my good friend Charles offered to answer the door for me. I followed at a little distance, and to my horror heard the unmistakeable voices of Molly and Jack.

'Surprise, surprise!' they chorused, and bustled past an open-mouthed Charles. Jack was carrying a hamper identical to the one I had given away the week before.

'Give and ye shall receive!' he sang heading towards the sitting room, while Molly embraced me with such gusto I almost lost my balance. With a jolly 'Hello, folks!' Jack placed the offering on the coffee table, and seating themselves comfortably the pair proceeded to recount in the fullest detail, with nothing too dull to mention, the history of our so-called friendship to my bewildered guests. Hardly drawing breath, they seemed unaware as one by one my friends slipped away, even Charles abandoning me with the excuse of an early morning start. It was two a.m. when I managed to persuade them into a local minicab, and, bleary-eyed and defeated, agreed to keep the hamper and 'eat up all my victuals like a good skinny girl!'

'And remember,' said Jack squeezing my shoulder, 'I'll always be there for you, no matter what!'

The situation was getting out of hand. Truth to tell I was feeling harassed by them, and knew I had to do something to stop it. Short of telling them in no uncertain terms that they were *personae non gratae* I could think of nothing, and, reluctant to grasp the nettle, I let the matter simmer. Then a week passed without any contact from them, then two. Two whole weeks of peace, I could scarcely believe it! One whole month went by, then two. Was it possible that I was free at last from their cloying attention? Could I finally put aside my lingering sense of guilt?

Then one morning the following letter arrived:

*Dear Sheila*

*I do hope you'll forgive me for not being in touch for so long but I didn't want to burden you with our problems. I'm sorry to have to tell you that a few months ago Jack was diagnosed with sclerosis of the liver. You can imagine what an unexpected blow it was. In spite of treatment we have now been told it is terminal and he has only a short time left. He is back at home with me now and I am caring for him. He is in quite some pain, but you know him he tries not to let on.*

*I know it's a lot to ask, but I wondered if you would pay him a visit? It would mean so much to both of us. You need not stay long as he gets tired very quickly. I will quite understand if you can't come for any reason, and I haven't told Jack I am writing so he won't be disappointed if you can't make it.*

*With fond wishes*

*Molly Edwards*

I was shocked, and more than grateful that I had delayed writing to them. I dropped Molly a short note suggesting that if it was convenient I could visit them the following Friday.

Jack was almost unrecognisable, lying on a sofa in their living room with a thin coverlet outlining his wasted shape. His face was gaunt, his skin pallid, and dark shadows set his eyes deep into his skull. Wisps of hair clung to his head in sweaty strands. He smiled with pleasure when I took his hand, but almost at once winced, gritting his teeth, his eyes squeezed shut.

'Sorry,' he managed.

'Oh Jack, please! Don't be sorry!'

Molly patted the armchair beside hers. 'Come and sit here, Sheila,' she said, 'He'll be all right in a minute. He jokes that they've left some open safety-pins in his gut and they stick into him when he moves!' Her short laugh sounded more like a sob.

And so Molly and I had a cup of tea and watched Jack as he struggled with his pain, slipping from time to time into a sleep that must have been a blessing. After a while I left, hugging Molly in silence. There was, after all, nothing to be said.

Molly was determined to make Jack's funeral a celebration rather than a sad affair. She requested that all the mourners wear their brightest summer outfits, and the ceremony in the crematorium was brief, with music chosen, as I recall, from *Carousel* and *The Sound of Music*. Afterwards in the car park Molly opened a picnic basket and handed out warm champagne in paper cups, something Jack in his working capacity would have looked down on. Indeed, perhaps he was! As we stood around in the sunshine Molly told me of a promise she had made to Jack just before he died. He had asked her to scatter his ashes as near to the stage door of the Drury Lane Theatre as she could, and she asked if I would be willing to join her when the time came. How could I refuse?

'It's ash-scattering time!' she yodelled quite cheerfully down the phone a few weeks later.

The ashes, she told me, had arrived in a container that she had found quite fetching, so she was now storing biscuits in it.

She was also inviting a work colleague and her husband to join us because they had loved musicals almost as much as she and Jack, and the two couples had spent some enjoyable times seeing them together.

'And I'm going to take you all out to dinner before the scattering,' she announced.

'Are you sure that's what you want?' I asked.

'I'm certain!' she replied firmly. 'It's something Jack would have approved of.'

'Well, in that case it might be sensible to meet for a late dinner somewhere in Covent Garden when there'll be fewer people around,' I suggested.

On the night the weather was appalling. Great sheets of rain cascaded down, churned by a relentless, biting wind. I squinted through the car windscreen and with luck on my side managed to find a parking space not too far from the designated restaurant. Fighting for control of my umbrella I hurried up the street and pushed open the restaurant door, gasping for breath as it slammed behind me. A slim, elegantly suited young man hurried towards me, relieving me with some distaste of the dripping umbrella and helping me out of my coat.

'Madam has a table booked?'

'Edwards,' I told him.

'Ah, two other guests are here already. This way please, follow me.'

A middle-aged couple stood at the bar, drinks in hand, looking somewhat ill at ease, and introduced themselves to me as Larry and Hilda Bateson. It wasn't long before they admitted they felt as uncomfortable as I did, not only about the dinner, but about the impending scattering. At last the restaurant door flew open and there stood Molly, shaking the rain vigorously from a small maroon umbrella while holding high a small, square maroon makeup case. The young man rushed forward anxiously, grabbing the offending brolly with one hand and reaching out with the other for the case.

'No you don't!' cried Molly, transferring the case from one hand to the other as he helped her out of her coat, and there she stood resplendent in a smart maroon suit, a vision of colour coordination. Seeing us at the bar she started towards us, the young man following, holding the wet coat and umbrella at arm's length.

'Would madam like to leave the case with me?'

'Absolutely not!' said Molly over her chicly padded shoulder, 'but we'll need an extra chair at the table.'

It seemed Jack was to join us for dinner.

A fifth chair was shoehorned in at the table for four to accommodate Jack's remains. This made us uncomfortably short of elbow room, but when Molly asked to be moved to a larger table, the manager was intransigent.

'No, madam!' he said firmly, 'we are completely booked this evening. One more chair is the best I can do.'

To make matters even more bizarre, Molly insisted on including the case in her conversation, addressing it with remarks like 'Didn't we?' or 'Wasn't it?' and 'Do you remember?' and after a while, I found myself almost expecting the case to reply!

Having decided we would leave the restaurant as late as we could I kept glancing surreptitiously at my watch, but the hands seemed hardly to move. The evening dragged on as the other diners dwindled away, and by the time we were on our third round of coffee it was all too clear the waiters were getting restless and it was time to leave. One look through the glass door confirmed what I had been dreading: the rain and wind were still as fierce as they had been earlier.

'Instead of all of us getting soaked, why don't I get the car and come back for you?' I suggested as brightly as I could. 'Then as we drive past the stage door, I'll slow down and Molly, you can scatter the ashes out of the window.'

Soon we were all seated in my suitably black car, with Larry and Hilda in the back, and Molly beside me, the makeup case cradled on her lap. I pulled over to allow a car behind me to pass, and, peering through the heavy rain, set off at a snail's pace down the almost deserted street.

'Come on then, Molly,' said Larry, tapping her on the shoulder, 'time to let him go.'

Molly opened the case, took out a small black plastic bag and an elegant pair of scissors, and carefully snipped off a corner.

'Goodbye, Jack darling,' she said. 'Enjoy!'

She wound the window down, and as she lifted the bag and shook its contents out a blast of wind and driving rain blew the ashes back into the car. Fumbling wildly, Molly managed to close the window but too late; we were all of us scattered and splattered, and smattered with ash. And the ash was wet; it stuck to our cheeks, it clung to our lips, it hung on our eyelids and covered our brows; our hair was speckled and salt-and-peppered; it even slid down inside clothes. The car had fared no better, with ash caught in every crevice and every surface pebble-dashed.

I pulled over, turned off the engine, and for one long, stricken moment we stared at one another, appalled. And as we tried to brush off the sticky grey cinders, we began to laugh. We laughed until our sides ached and breathing came hard and tears of mirth streaked our cheeks. And as I passed round the box of tissues I kept handy just in case, Molly spoke.

'Well,' she said, 'Jack did say he'd always be there for you, Sheila, and it looks like he meant it!'

Molly wasn't wrong. No amount of vacuuming could clear the invasive ash from my car, and as I handed the keys over to its new owner, I noticed a small flake that had settled itself on the driver's seat.

# DUELOGUE

It's been oh, such fun,
Aren't I just the lucky one!
The time has simply flown…

                        Can't wait to be alone.

What was that? What did you say?
Sorry, I was miles away.

                        Wish I was… I'm not.
                        Lord, how fat he's got!
                        What did I ever see…

Pardon me? my diary?
I just don't seem to have it here.

                        Go out again with him? No fear!

Thanks for this evening,
You've not changed at all!
Let's not make plans
I'll just give you a call.

                        Call you a chauvinist,
                        Call you a bore.
                        When we were married
                        You called me a whore!
                        Oh-oh, *quelle surprise*!
                        His hand's between my knees…
          It's his subtle way to show what's on his mind.
Dear God, I would have to be deaf, dumb, and blind!

Do you know…

I never will understand men as a race.
The way they behave is a bloody disgrace!
I married this idiot, should have known better
He can't do addition, he can't write a letter,
But so good in bed that I married the berk,
Then realised it was *me* doing the work!

I ironed his shirts and I bought all his sox,
I wore sexy undies and elegant frocks,
While he sat about with his beer and his belly
And goggled at garbage produced on the telly.

I'd finally had it to here all the way
So I said to my best friend (who's splendidly gay)
I'm leaving him! Going! He said, about time!
As a matter of fact (I'm not bitchy) but I'm
About to say something that may cause you pain…
He's having a torrid affair with Lorraine!

Affair with Lorraine? What a sod! What a swine!
What a blankety blank (well they censored that line)
So I left him. Since when life's been fine.

Well…

When I say 'fine', I mean fine to be free,
Free to go anywhere, free to be me.
Free to do anything, or anyone,
Trouble is most of it never got done.

I just sat on my butt and I thought of my fate
And I realised how much I needed a mate.
Began to regret that I'd left him although
He's a sod. Still, it's best with the devil you know.

Then he called me and asked if I'd come out to dine,
And I'm here, and my knees and his hands intertwine.
I must say, in spite of it all he's got charm…
We may be divorced but so what? Where's the harm?
It may be frustration, it may be the wine…
The hell! Who cares?

Your place or mine?

# RICHARD

The skirt was torn! She couldn't believe it. The commissionaire had held the door open for her with a smile of admiration, and of course she'd been aware of how elegant she looked in her new dress with its handkerchief-panelled skirt, so instead of looking where she was going she'd tripped on the first step up into the thickly carpeted lobby and felt the fabric catch under her foot. Now she sat on the edge of a dressing-table stool in the ladies' rest room, all pink and plush and soft lighting, miserably blinking back tears of rage and frustration as she inspected the damage. Sure enough, one corner of a front panel was torn. Damn! Why hadn't she looked where she was going? She had bought the dress especially for the occasion. It had been ridiculously expensive, costing the entire fee for yesterday's filming. Five hundred pounds! She must have been mad! Still, Hesta reasoned, she had had nothing suitable to wear. Richard had said it was an important dinner, and she certainly didn't want to let him down. She couldn't suppress a wry smile. Was it serendipity that the film location on Friday happened to be in a very smart dress shop in Golders Green?

The TV commercial had been for a new brand of cosmetics, and the 'star', a worryingly thin, pretty model, seemed to neither know nor care what was going on around her. Hesta's role as saleslady had been to lurk dimly in the background, and it was through sheer boredom that, during the afternoon tea break, she had found herself browsing through the rails of elaborate cocktail dresses. She certainly hadn't intended to make a purchase, although the question of what she would wear on her date with Mr Richard Trotter, millionaire, had been on her mind. As she moved idly to a third rail of flounces and glitter, her eye had been caught by the glint of darker tones, purple and magenta. Carefully pulling the garment free from its neighbours, she had shaken the dress out. It was georgette of the deepest blue, the skirt made of floating handkerchief panels, and around the low scoop neck was a band of oil-slick-coloured pearls. It seemed about her size. Then she looked at the price tag, placed the dress firmly back on the rack and walked away, while a still, small voice whispered that surely there couldn't be any harm in trying it on.

The shop proprietor, a fierce-looking woman with hennaed hair, was sitting on the sidelines in a canvas chair staring disapprovingly at the disruption to her domain. Hesta approached her cautiously.

'Excuse me.'

'What?' she snapped. Hesta hesitated.

'Er… can I have a word with you?'

'What is it?' the woman said irritably.

'I hope you don't mind, but I couldn't resist having a wander round to look at your stunning clothes.'

'Oh yes?' she said suspiciously.

'Yes,' Hesta continued, smiling, she hoped, disarmingly, 'and I've found this really lovely dress on that rail over there,' she pointed. The woman stared at Hesta saying nothing, and nonplussed, Hesta felt she ought to explain.

'You see,' she said quickly, 'I met someone who's invited me to a very smart dinner tomorrow night, and I really need to…'

'You want to try it on?' The response was brusque.

'Well, I thought…'

'Yes or no?'

'Yes.'

'You'll have to wait until this filming fiasco is over, and you'll have to be quick. Once all this...' she waved a hand in the air, 'is cleared, my girls will be here to get things back to normal. Show me the dress.'

She stood up, looking around for somewhere to dispose of the polystyrene cup she held in a red-taloned hand, then thrust it at Hesta.

'Get rid of this, will you. I don't want any accidents near my stock.'

Hesta added it to a collection of abandoned cups standing on a metal box close by.

'Show me,' the woman had said, and that had been that.

'You had some accident?'

Hesta was aware of a figure in an overall sitting in the shadows behind her. The voice was warm and friendly, the accent sounded Jamaican.

'My own fault. Silly!'

She pulled a tissue out of the satin-covered box in front of her and dabbed carefully at the corners of her eyes. No point in ruining her makeup as well. Holding the panel up for closer inspection, 'I think I'm going to have to cut this bit off,' she said. 'You don't happen to have a pair of scissors handy do you?'

'Only nail scissors,' came the reply. 'That do?'

'Yes, anything!' Hesta said gratefully. 'Thanks.'

She snipped at the ragged fabric with small careful bites of the curved blades, and wondered whether being late for their meeting in the hotel bar would annoy her new acquaintance. She had only met him the previous Wednesday night in the crowded foyer of a West End theatre, introduced by Eric Wittenberg, a friend of hers of long standing. It had been the opening of a much acclaimed American musical, and Eric, a distinguished financier, enjoyed investing in theatre productions however ill-advised some of them turned out to be. He'd invited Hesta to accompany him to his latest folly because his wife, the beautiful and successful authoress Constance Walker, was away on a book-signing tour, and, not for the first time, Hesta had been delighted to accept the role as stand-in. There was a time when friends had considered Hesta and Eric to be an 'item', but that had never quite been the case. As fond of him as she was Hesta could never think of him romantically, and eventually their relationship had settled into a comfortable and lasting friendship. She remembered with some amusement the night Eric had arrived to take her out to dinner, but instead, whiskey in hand, had sat her down on her sofa and told her that his plans for the evening had changed. Apologising profusely, he'd said he was on his way to propose marriage to Constance, and that he was sure she would accept him. Then he'd downed his drink and driven off, excited as a child looking forward to Christmas. As Hesta, still dressed in her smart little black number and three-inch stilettos, munched a cheese sandwich in her kitchen she had shaken her head, sceptical as to the outcome of Eric's proposal. But she'd been wrong, and much to the surprise of many, Constance had accepted him. Indeed now, three years later, the partnership was proving highly successful.

That night Eric had waved enthusiastically at a man standing at the other end of the bar with two attractive young women.

'There's my old friend Richard!' he'd said enthusiastically, launching his large frame into the crowd and forcing them to give way, beaming as he went and quite oblivious to the irritation he was causing. Hesta was used to his bluff manners by now, and followed in his wake smiling apologetically. When Eric reached the group of three he'd patted the man briskly on the back, and he had responded with obvious pleasure. For some reason Hesta felt drawn to him. His eyes, she noted, were surprisingly blue and his mouth sensual, curving slightly upwards on one side, giving him a look of wry amusement.

'Aren't you going to introduce me?' he'd asked Eric.

'Of course, old man,' said Eric. 'This is Hesta Ash. Hesta, meet a good friend of mine, Richard Trotter. Hesta kindly agreed to play stand-in tonight for my wife,' adding, 'not in every sense, you understand!' And he'd laughed raucously, as was his wont, turning a few disapproving heads. His friend had responded, 'I'm relieved to hear it!' and as he glanced at Hesta her pulse quickened. The two attractive young women were introduced as his nieces, and a feeling of relief had swept through her, closely followed by a sense of the ridiculous. Here she was with a man she had only just been introduced to, and she was behaving like a teenager! Then to her embarrassment Eric had wagged an admonishing finger at his friend, saying: 'I'm surprised at you, Richard, surely you recognise Hesta? She's a well-known and very fine actress!'

'Of course! Now I recognise you!' Richard had said. 'Although in my defence, may I say your screen image doesn't do you justice.'

'I'm glad it's not the other way around!' Hesta had replied, and as they laughed, for no particular reason she had put a hand on his arm but withdrawn it quickly. Too late! Richard had noted the gesture, and as he held her gaze Hesta felt a spark pass between them. Flustered, she had turned to Eric and suggested they go in, and as they moved away she'd felt a touch on her arm.

'I'm glad we met.'

She had turned, but Richard was already following his nieces towards the auditorium entrance.

During the interval Hesta had felt sure that Richard would seek her out but there was no sign of him, and it was with a mixture of disappointment and some relief that she told herself she'd probably escaped another opportunity to make a fool of herself. Her last relationship had proved to be a fiasco, very much like the one before that, and she had promised herself she would stick to having only friends and acquaintances and keep her emotions under control, and her bedroom firmly out of bounds.

Sitting together in their late-night taxi, Hesta and Eric had discussed the merits of the evening's entertainment. Then, telling herself she was simply curious, she had asked him about his friend Richard.

'Richard S. Trotter, clever man, fine business brain,' he'd said. 'He's a real-estate millionaire with his own company in the city. Known him for years. Keen on theatre and mad about opera. Pretty girls, those nieces of his, don't you think?'

'Very,' Hesta agreed. Then trying to sound casual, she'd asked, 'I wonder why his wife wasn't with him tonight.'

'Which one?' Eric guffawed. 'He's been married several times. Twice, maybe three times. I've no idea what his present status is.' Then leaning towards her with a knowing smile he'd patted her hand.

'Interested?' he'd asked.

'Don't be silly!' she'd replied, glad of the darkness in the cab.

'You are!' Eric had roared triumphantly. 'Well, you wilful woman, I don't suppose I can stop you!'

'Eric dear, there's no point in trying to stop me since nothing has started,' she had countered tartly, 'or, indeed,' she had added, 'is likely to!'

The next morning Hesta had been expecting a call from her agent with details of the television advert she was due to shoot the following day, so when the phone rang she was surprised to hear an unfamiliar voice.

'Can I speak with Miss Ash?'

'Speaking.'

'Miss Ash, this is Eric Wittenberg's secretary. I've just had a phone call from a friend of his, a Mr Richard Trotter.'

'Oh?' Hesta's heart quickened.

'He asked to be put through to Mr Wittenberg, and after they'd spoken Mr Wittenberg came through to me, and…'

'Yes?' She tried to keep her voice steady.

'Apparently Mr Trotter asked Mr Wittenberg if he would mind giving him your phone number. Mr Wittenberg asked me to give you a ring and...'

'Yes, that's fine!'

'Sorry?' The voice had an edge to it, and Hesta realised she might have sounded a bit short.

'What I meant to say was by all means do give him... Mr Trotter, that is... my number. And thank you so much for calling me, I really do appreciate it.' She mentally blushed at her over-effusive performance.

'Not at all.' The secretary seemed somewhat placated.

'Oh, and will you thank Mr Wittenberg for the taxi ride home. Tell him I'm sure he's looking forward as much as I am to the outcome of last night's conversation.'

She didn't have long to wait. Ten minutes later the phone rang.

'Miss Ash? Hesta? Richard Trotter here.' His voice was soft, warm, sexy. 'I'm delighted you agreed to let me call you. I was wondering if you were free this coming Saturday night. Not much notice, I'm afraid, but it's an invitation I've only just received myself... a useful business colleague so I can't refuse. It's likely to be a dull affair, a private dinner party at the Savoy, but it would make it so much more pleasant if you agreed to accompany me. And if you'll allow me, I'll make it up to you by taking you to one of my favourite restaurants next Monday evening when we can get to know one another a little better. That is if you can bear the thought of my company on two occasions following on so closely. What do you say?'

'This coming Saturday night? I think it might be all right... let me just check.'

She had sat holding the phone in her lap, then after a short pause lifted the receiver to her ear.

'Sorry to keep you waiting. I have something pencilled in for the weekend, but I'm sure I can change it for another day. All right, I'd be happy to accept your invitation.'

'Excellent! You've cheered me up no end. Meet you in the American bar at the Savoy on Saturday evening. About seven?'

And now here she was at ten past seven, not in the bar, but in the ladies' room feeling sorry for herself. She stood up, straightened her dress, and crossed to the full-length mirror. The torn panel hardly showed... or was it just the reassurance of the dim lighting? Well, there was nothing more to be done. She looked at herself critically. Perhaps she had applied too much makeup for what, she supposed, was to be a sober business dinner, but she excused herself on the grounds of what might be acceptable for an actress.

She found Richard Trotter sitting at a low table in the American bar, and although she was fifteen minutes late he waved her apology aside and handed her a tall, slim glass.

'I hope you don't mind, but I took the liberty of ordering champagne. You look like a champagne girl to me. Am I right?'

'Absolutely... it's my favourite tipple.'

'Mine too, although I wouldn't admit it to my beer-guzzling colleagues! I hope you won't find this evening's company tedious. If the conversation gets too corporate just think of England. I'm sure you'll charm them.' Then he lifted his glass. 'And may I say,' he leaned towards her and spoke softly, 'you do look stunning!'

As she snuggled down into her duvet that night, she decided the evening had been a success. There were eight other people in the private dining room, and although the other two women at the table had both worn smart, well-cut trouser suits making her feel distinctly overdressed, Richard's compliment had boosted her confidence. She had been placed between two middle-aged men who discussed matters of investment as though she wasn't there, but after a glass or two of the excellent wine served with the minimal portions of *haute cuisine*, she relaxed a little and enjoyed the wickedly conspiratorial glances Richard threw her way now and again from the other end of the table. At the end of the evening as they walked through the hotel foyer, Richard had said apologetically: 'I have a ridiculously early meeting in the morning... do you mind if I forfeit the pleasure of driving you home? May I get you a taxi?' And without waiting for her reply, he had waved at the commissionaire standing at the door. Then to Hesta's embarrassment he had taken a leather wallet from the inside pocket of his jacket.

'I hope you'll accept the taxi fare. It's by way of an apology.'

'Oh no, please, there's no need,' she had said, but, 'Nonsense,' he had insisted, 'there's no question about it. I shall be most unhappy if you don't accept it.' And with that he had taken her hand and placed a crisp, new twenty-pound note in it. Now that she thought about it, it had rather tarnished the evening, but then she remembered how he had closed her fingers around it with his, holding them there for a moment longer than he needed.

'I'm very much looking forward to our dinner date on Monday. Still on, I hope?'

Hesta had nodded.

'Splendid. I shall phone you on Monday morning and arrange to pick you up at... shall we say about seven thirty?'

Again she had nodded. Then he had leaned towards her, brushed her cheek lightly with his lips, and... had she really felt his hand linger for a moment on her breast? No, surely not! But she couldn't be certain.

On Monday evening Hesta took care not to over-dress. She was, as usual, ready early, and not wanting to crease the narrow skirt and stylish jacket, sat stiffly on the settee in her living room sipping a small glass of chilled white wine. When the doorbell rang, her two lively collies headed excitedly for the hallway. *Oh Lord, I hope he likes dogs!* She hadn't mentioned them when he'd phoned that morning. Well, too late now. She opened the door, holding it slightly ajar.

'Sorry, I should have warned you. Do you like dogs?'

'Love 'em! Bring 'em on! Only let me give you these first.'

He pushed the door open and handed her an enormous bunch of yellow roses, not seeming to mind the dogs jumping up on his immaculate suit.

'These are beautiful, thank you so much!' Hesta was overwhelmed. 'Come in! Now, can I offer you a glass of white wine while I put these in water? I'll put the dogs in the kitchen.'

Richard followed her into the sitting room and, throwing himself into an armchair, stretched out and closed his eyes.

'Long day! The only thing that got me through it was looking forward to seeing you.'

Hesta knew, of course, that he wasn't being completely honest, but she didn't care one bit.

He drove her to a discreetly smart restaurant in Regent's Park, in his Mercedes two-seater sports convertible (a car Hesta had always coveted), and although she had always thought of it as a young person's car, she decided it rather suited him. During the journey Richard seemed to want to know a lot about her. Had she been married? Only once? Was she divorced? To all of those she'd answered yes, and no to any children. Only dogs, she'd added with a laugh, saying she thought she wasn't very good at relationships. No sooner had she said it, she had regretted it. It was, after all, hardly the best way to begin any sort of friendship, even if, judging from her past record, it was true.

'That's enough about me,' she said quickly. 'How about you?'

Richard told her he'd been married twice before and had an only daughter by his first wife. He admitted he didn't like being on his own, and although he had had several affairs he would much prefer to be married.

'Mind you,' he added, 'I'll probably choose the wrong partner yet again. I'm forty-one years old, you'd have thought I'd have learnt by now. I've probably got more money than sense!'

Well to Hesta he seemed to be very sensible, so she could only assume that he was very rich! Then as he opened the car door for her, he asked her how old she was. Just like that! And before she had time to consider her reply, 'I'm forty,' she said.

'Oh dear,' he said, closing the car door behind her, 'too old for me!'

Imagine how she felt! She followed him to the restaurant door hoping he would say something that would turn this hurtful observation into a witty remark of some sort, but instead he opened the door, and with a slight bow ushered her in.

The lighting in the wood-panelled dining room was low, the background music soft and unobtrusive, Richard was attentive and amusing, and before long Hesta had quite forgotten what he'd said. Watching him across the table she decided that though he wasn't by any means tall, dark and handsome she found him not only attractive, but quite sexy. He was, in fact, rather stocky, and not much taller than Hesta herself. His greying hair was straight and cut short, and like a schoolboy's refused to lie flat at the crown, which she found rather endearing. He had a slow smile and a witty sense of humour, and soon Hesta was charmed and enchanted.

It was as they lingered over coffee that Richard leaned towards her, and placing his hand over hers asked softly: 'Would you mind if I fell in love with you?'

That is exactly what he said! Hesta's eyes widened in surprise; her heart began to race and there was a singing and a ringing in her ears. She felt faint. And then he said, 'Actually, at the moment I'm in love with someone else. She's a lot younger than me. I've asked her several times, but she won't marry me.'

Now you'd have thought that would have brought Hesta to her senses pretty sharply, but no. All Hesta, poor, silly, Hesta could hear, were the waves of romance breaking on the shore of her lonely, beached life, so she missed that last bit, and let her heart go.

The next few months flew by. When they were together Richard would get out his diary and page through it, then ask casually what are you doing on the whatever of whenever, and Hesta would get out her empty little diary, pretend to page through it, and say yes, she thought she might be free. Then he'd go on to another date and so on until she would laugh and say, hold on, that's quite enough for the moment! Richard took Hesta to private viewings of art exhibitions, and to concerts and to the theatre, and they always sat in the very best seats; and afterwards they would dine at the smartest, most expensive restaurants. But most of all, Richard loved the opera. In fact music seemed to fill his life. It was almost an obsession with him! He played music endlessly… in his car, in his flat, and in every room in his country house. He played it while he worked and he played it while he didn't work and he played it very loud. So loud that Hesta couldn't hear herself speak. Or him. So she didn't and neither did he. And sometimes when she really wanted to say something important to him and couldn't be heard, she would wonder if that was the very reason he kept the music playing.

Richard lived in a spacious flat in the best part of town as well as owning a lovely old country house in the Cotswolds, and that was where they spent most weekends. In spite of the many large rooms in the house, Hesta and Richard spent most of their time in a small study furnished with probably the only casual and comfortable chairs in the house. Here they would pass the time reading or watching television, and even eating their meals. A rather dubious couple lived in a converted flat on the top floor, and looked after the house and grounds during the week. The wife was a dour woman with shifty eyes, while the husband, a sharp-nosed, gaunt man with a scruffy beard, seemed to undress Hesta with his eyes whenever she encountered him, something she found most unnerving.

On Friday evenings Hesta would drive the dogs in her scruffy old car, while Richard would race up the motorway in his sporty two-seater. He had allocated her her very own bedroom, which was very kind and generous but odd, because at night they slept together in his rather grand four-poster. Still, her bedroom had its own bathroom with one of those big old-fashioned baths that sat in the middle of the room on ball-and-claw feet, and she loved soaking in it, while the dogs snuffled around and finally settled, eyeing her dolefully. The dogs were no longer allowed to sleep upstairs at night; not since that very first night when the youngest dog Ned had decided to mark out the entire first floor as his territory. When Hesta discovered the mishaps the following morning,, not only in all of the bedrooms but also on the landing, she was horrified. To make matters worse, the floors were covered throughout with thick-pile cream carpeting. Richard seemed quite sanguine and understanding, but Hesta knew he wasn't too pleased, to say the least. She decided to hire one of those heavy-duty carpet-cleaning machines, and spent the following weekend pulling and pushing and scrubbing and sweating and filling and refilling its weighty water tank with its special solution. Early on she realised with alarm that the clean bits made the rest of the carpet look dirty, so she had no choice but to scrub clean every inch. It took the entire weekend, and when Sunday drew to a close, Richard finally emerged and mounted the stairs to inspect her handiwork. Hesta, wan and exhausted and soaked in chemical suds, stood proudly by her trusty machine, and Richard patted her on the behind (a gesture she was beginning to find annoying) saying: 'My goodness, I didn't expect you to have done the entire floor! No wonder it took you so long.'

It soon became clear that Richard wasn't the most communicative of men... in fact he didn't really like talking at all. When he did speak he usually spoke of Sandra, the woman he was in love with. He talked of how besotted he was with her and that at the moment their relationship was purely platonic but he hoped she would eventually love him, and how, in spite of all the lovely gifts he'd given her, she was determined to get to the top of her profession (whatever that was) on her own merit, and she certainly didn't want people thinking she'd married a rich man who was a good fifteen years her senior as a short cut to success. Apparently she did mention that her mother wasn't too pleased by the age gap, and had told her that when she married it should be to someone nearer her own age so that they could have lots of children and grow old together; and Sandra said she always took her mother's advice. But she had told Richard that she was very fond of him and that things might change, and that you never knew! Richard was certain she would come round to his way of thinking in time, certain that love would conquer all. (Well, we all want what we can't have, and the more we can't have it, the more we know we simply cannot live without it. Ah, poor Richard.)

And poor Hesta. Because Richard (who was nothing if not the most honest, as well as the most generous man she'd ever known) had made it clear from the start that she was just a substitute. For the moment, at any rate. Richard didn't exactly rule out the possibility that things might, just might change, but it did depend on young Sandra. And Sandra, who was getting lots of attention as well as the odd present from time to time, didn't seem in a hurry to make up her mind. It seemed when Richard had told her about Hesta, she'd assured him that she was still giving his offer of marriage serious thought. What a muddle! And it was becoming even more of a muddle because by now Hesta had fallen deeply in love with Richard. She loved the shape of the back of his head, and the way the hair on the crown just wouldn't lie flat, and she loved the way he stood with his legs planted firmly apart as he looked up at the crop of plums on the trees in his orchard. She didn't even mind when the sound of his stentorian snoring kept her awake at night as she lay beside him. But there was something she did mind. She minded that he never showed her any affection, rather like her friend Stella's erstwhile lover, Everard. No, Richard never held her hand or touched her affectionately, and she did ache for some indication that he cared for her, even a little. Still, she knew that because he was such an honest man he didn't want to mislead her in any way, and after all that was admirable. Wasn't it?

By now Hesta was getting used to Richard's odd ways. He never seemed to notice what she wore, and never told her she looked nice; he sometimes forgot to thank her for doing things for him, like the time when he had to entertain some Very Important People and she'd cleaned his flat and filled it with flowers and left plates of canapés covered with clingfilm. He talked even less and played his music even louder but it made no difference. Hesta loved him. And then, for no particular reason, she began to feel the first pricking of a tiny splinter of doubt and mistrust catching at the fabric of their affair. She knew from past experience that unless she plucked it out as quickly as she could it would double and trouble itself into a wedge that would split them apart, but she couldn't help worrying about the silences between them, and she wondered if Richard was bored with her, or if she had said something to offend him, or, indeed, done something to annoy him. She knew he had problems he couldn't discuss with her because she knew nothing of his world of business, and she understood exactly how he felt about Sandra because that was exactly how she felt about him: she loved him, and she couldn't have him. But she also knew that he needed someone, and as long as she didn't make waves all would be well. Until, that is, Sandra made her mind up.

One evening, as they sat silent in a smart local Italian restaurant, Richard suddenly said: 'I think it's time you had a new car.'

It was true. Hesta's car was rather old and had been giving her quite a lot of trouble recently. What's more, it was just an ordinary four-wheeler, not exactly ideal for ferrying three dogs around.

'I have a contact who'll help you choose something suitable,' he said, 'then I'll transfer the money into your bank account.'

'Oh no,' Hesta protested, 'I couldn't possibly accept!' and meant it, but Richard insisted.

'Just think of it as a birthday present. When is your birthday, by the way?'

'February the fifteenth,' said Hesta.

There you are then, a belated birthday gift.'

It was the longest conversation they'd had in a while, and it was such an exciting and generous present she could hardly believe it. She decided it showed such thoughtfulness that Richard must care for her, even if he didn't actually put it into words; she'd been worried for no good reason and felt reassured.

The following Friday evening, thrilled and delighted, Hesta drove the dogs to the country in her shiny new silver estate. Next day, as they were sitting in the small study, Richard as usual working on some papers, glasses poised on the end of his nose, while Hesta read the morning papers and the dogs lazed at her feet, Richard looked up and said: 'It looks as though we'll still be together in a month or so, so I think we should take a holiday together. I'll drive through France and Italy… I'd quite enjoy a break on my own… and you can join me when I get to Florence. It's a glorious city, and once we've explored it we can drive back taking our time, stopping off to enjoy the local food and wine, and take in the culture and the glorious countryside.'

First the car and now this! Hesta could hardly breathe.

She began making plans, spending money she couldn't afford on designer summer clothes and expensive sandals, determined to make Richard proud to be seen with her. And then one night he told her that he'd mentioned their plans to take a holiday together to Sandra, and she had told him that she quite understood he needed a break, and when he came back they ought to have a serious talk.

'I think,' he finished, 'she is close to agreeing to marry me.'

Imagine how Hesta felt. Her stomach had no pit, her world had no purpose, and her heart was a rock dragging her down. And the holiday they had planned was just a week away.

'What about Italy?' Hesta managed with difficulty, her mouth dry.

'Oh, I discussed it with her and she was generous enough to insist we still go, so it shouldn't affect our plans.'

The next few days were painful and difficult. Hesta didn't want to be on holiday with him knowing he would rather be with someone else, and it crossed her mind that going on this holiday might well have been the reason Sandra had changed her mind. She wished she could talk to Richard about it, but she knew she couldn't because he would never talk about anything important, so she had to wrestle with the problem on her own. After a lot of soul searching she reasoned that apart from anything else Richard needed a holiday. He got up early and worked hard all day, and his weekends were spent poring over documents. Plans were in place and probably paid for, so all in all she felt she had no choice; she decided they should go away as planned.

Richard's sports car could comfortably accommodate himself and one passenger, and he was adamant there was no room for two suitcases. He suggested that Hesta pack the minimum of clothing she would need into a reasonably sized suitcase they could share (not too big, not too small), and bring it to his flat the evening before he was due to drive off on his own. That night, having cooked him dinner she sat cross-legged on his big double bed with the suitcase half full of her things in front of her. She tried to be as jolly as she could, helping him decide what clothes he should pack. All things considered they were having a reasonably good time when the extension phone in the bedroom rang. Richard looked at her and she looked at Richard, and it was clear exactly who it was ringing.

'I'll just go downstairs for a minute,' Hesta said quickly. The last thing she wanted to hear was any conversation between Richard and Sandra, and she knew Richard must feel much as she did. Off the bed she leapt and down the stairs she ran, and as she went into the sitting room she heard the two of them speaking to one another. It seemed Richard had left his answering machine on with the volume turned up. As soon as she realised what was happening she knew she should walk out of the room. But she didn't. She stayed where she was and she listened. And what she heard was two people very much in love telling each other how much they'd miss one another while one of them was away. When the conversation ended and Richard put down the phone, the silence filled Hesta's head to bursting. She sat still as death; she had never felt so alone. After a while she walked slowly back upstairs. Richard was folding his clothes into a neat pile ready to pack, and as she entered the bedroom he looked up at her and smiled. He was about to speak when he saw that something was very wrong.

'Hesta...'

But before he could say any more, Hesta interrupted.

'Sorry,' she managed, 'the answering machine... I heard...'

Richard moved towards her with his arms outstretched; it was the first time he had made any gesture of affection since she'd known him.

'No!' she choked, and fled down the staircase and across the hallway, and as she wrenched open the front door, for reasons she could never explain nor credit, she called out, 'See you in Florence.'

As she slowly drove home she wondered why on earth she'd said it. The last thing she wanted now was to go away with him. She thought how silly she had been wasting her hard-earned money on expensive clothes, particularly since Richard never noticed what she wore, nor cared. And for the first time she realised that for two whole weeks she was going to have to pretend she was having a good time. And presumably so would Richard. It was a ridiculous situation. Unless... what if she could persuade Sandra to fly to Florence instead of her, and spend this holiday with Richard! There was no harm in trying, was there? All she had to do was get hold of Sandra's phone number and suggest it to her. She began to feel a little better. When she got home she wondered if Richard would at least phone to see if she was all right, but of course he didn't. Well, she thought, what did you expect?

The next day was one of the hardest she'd ever had to get through, not only because of the impossible situation she found herself in, but also because she had overheard Richard tell Sandra he would phone her before he left in the morning, and when her own phone stayed silent, she felt another twist of the knife. That afternoon she rang Richard's secretary and managed to wheedle Sandra's phone number out of her. At first Sandra seemed to have no idea who Hesta was, but when the penny dropped she agreed quite happily to Hesta's suggestion that they meet up the next evening in the bar of a hotel in town. There was no phone call from Richard that evening either, but Hesta guessed he would be phoning Sandra, because she knew a man travelling on his own and in love with a woman would certainly want to talk to her. And that being the case, Sandra would be bound to tell Richard of Hesta's phone call and the arranged meeting.

The following night a nervous but determined Hesta took the hotel lift to the top-floor lounge overlooking the city lights, ordered herself a large gin and tonic, and waited. She waited and she waited and she realised that after all, Sandra wasn't going to turn up. Even so, knowing she was wasting good time, she waited even longer. And she was sure that it was Richard who had advised Sandra not to turn up. Not that he would actually have told her not to, he was much too much of a diplomat for that. No, he would have said something like, 'You must do as you think fit, and of course it's entirely up to you, but there doesn't seem much point in you two meeting.' And he would probably have added that Hesta would understand if she didn't turn up and would probably have realised it was for the best. And so Hesta left.

She wasn't surprised when, soon after she got home, the phone rang and Richard told her he was somewhere in France having had a wonderful meal and an excellent bottle of claret (and, Hesta surmised, a long and intimate conversation with Sandra to check whether she had followed his advice!). Now any sensible woman would have taken this opportunity to finish the affair, but like a train whose brakes have failed Hesta couldn't stop herself from careening headlong towards disaster.

Richard met her at Florence airport. He seemed offhand and irritable, and as they drove to the hotel the music in the car blared out louder than ever. He had booked into the most beautiful old villa, set high on a mountainside overlooking the city. In the evenings, caressed by the warm, fragrant air, they would sit at table on the long, carved wooden balcony, eating the most excellent Italian dishes and drinking the finest wines. Later they would go up to the spacious bedroom with its dark antique furniture and wooden shutters, stand side by side in the marbled bathroom, each at their individual washbasins, and then climb into the large, comfortable four-poster bed. Their days were spent marvelling at the city with its glorious churches and museums and squares, and they picnicked on ancient steps, slicing into salamis and tearing off chunks of loaves they had bought at nearby markets. They tried different cheeses and tasted the cheap local wines sold in bottles with no labels.

Hesta had always wanted a suede jacket but never been able to afford one. Now here in Florence, wherever they went they were surrounded by shops selling leather goods at ridiculously low prices. Hesta wanted to take advantage of the opportunity, but worried that if she mentioned it Richard might think she was hinting that he should buy a jacket for her, and that was certainly not what she wanted. One afternoon as they strolled down a shady cobbled alley, Hesta caught sight of just the jacket she had in mind. She stopped to look at it while Richard walked ahead.

'Come on!' he called over his shoulder.

'Just a minute,' Hesta answered, 'I want to look at this jacket.'

Richard, who by now was several paces ahead, stopped and turned.

'Come on. You don't want to buy any leather goods here.'

'Why not?' she asked, walking reluctantly away from the shop.

'Well, for a start the quality will be inferior,' he said, 'and you'd have to declare it at the border. Not only will that delay us unnecessarily, but by the time you've paid the tax, it won't have been worth it.'

Hesta wasn't at all sure that he was right, but she was still as in love with him as ever, and just being with him meant everything; the jacket would have to go on hold.

As already mentioned, Richard hardly ever spoke, which by definition meant neither did Hesta. They talked a little about the food they ate and the wine they drank and the wonders they beheld, but they never talked about anything that mattered, at least to Hesta. It was like being with someone she didn't know at all well, and having to be constantly on her best behaviour. Meanwhile Sandra's haunting spirit was ever present. Hesta was now certain that Richard not only knew of the arranged meeting with Sandra, but had engineered her decision not to turn up, and this deceit was an almost tangible barrier between them. From time to time Richard would disappear for rather a long time, making some feeble excuse or other about changing the CDs in his car, or buying some more bottled water in spite of the handy room service. Fed up with this deception, on one occasion Hesta had crept down the stairs after him, and saw him in the phone booth in the foyer, animated, his face aglow with pleasure. The quickest, surest way to ruin the holiday would be to mention anything about it, so she swallowed what little pride she had left, but it fermented away inside her until she felt if it wasn't aired soon, she would explode!

One balmy evening as they sat on the balcony after a particularly good dinner, Richard seemed to be in an unusually expansive mood. He actually talked a little about this and that, and Hesta thought to herself: this is my opportunity… it's now or never. Taking her courage in both hands, she told him everything. She told him she understood exactly how he felt about Sandra because she felt just the same about him, and she admitted that she had dreaded coming on this holiday because she knew he'd so much rather have been with Sandra. She explained that she had asked Sandra to meet her, not to make mischief, but to persuade Sandra to go to Italy with him in her place. Light-headed with the relief of her confession, Hesta added recklessly, 'I know Sandra must have told you I asked her to meet me, and I know it must have been you who persuaded her not to turn up. The only reason I came on holiday was because I knew you needed a break and you wouldn't have enjoyed it on your own.'

Then she told him how much she loved him.

Richard sat silent for a long moment, then he got up. 'I'm going for a walk,' he said shortly. 'I suggest you go to the room.' And he left her sitting there feeling bleak and empty.

She went upstairs as she'd been told, and after an hour she climbed into the grand four-poster bed and waited. At last Richard came in, and without a word undressed, turned out the light and got into bed, and there they lay side by side, rigid and still. It was a long, long night. Early the next morning Richard got up, and after a shower came and sat down on the edge of the bed.

'I'm afraid I don't want to spend time with anyone who thinks Sandra and I are schemers and liars,' he said. 'The best thing we can do is leave here as soon as possible and drive back home.'

'But I don't understand why you're so angry with me!' cried Hesta. 'I was trying to please you!'

'Don't make me say things I'll regret,' Richard retorted icily. 'Let's just say I don't like your mind, and I don't like the way you think.'

'Oh please don't do this! Please don't let it end this way!' Hesta pleaded. She had abandoned any pride she may have had and simply didn't care. And neither, apparently, did Richard.

The day that followed was painful. Hesta felt hollow with misery, while Richard remained aloof and cold. He even seemed to enjoy her discomfort, tucking into a hearty breakfast, and chatting as though there was nothing amiss. Hesta had the distinct feeling that he was pleased at the prospect of getting back home, and it crossed her mind that perhaps Richard had deliberately used last night as an excuse to get back to Sandra. But she knew only too well Richard had always been straight with her and, feeling ashamed, she put the thought out of her head. She decided to remove her belongings from the shared suitcase, stuffing them into a laundry bag she found in the wardrobe; and by mid morning the car was packed and the long drive home began. The CDs played constantly and loudly until Hesta felt the sounds were spilling out of her ears. Speeding along the motorway there was barely time to read the signposts naming the places they had planned to visit on their journey homeward. Pisa, Bologna, Modena, Reggio all whizzed by as Richard stared ahead, a deep, icy chasm between them, while Hesta clutched a handful of coins he had handed her, ready to pay the tolls.

Just before Parma Richard pulled up for petrol and suggested they have a bite to eat in the Le Routier close by. She had no appetite, but feeling she should show willing, Hesta trundled reluctantly after him, tray in hand, choosing a small Danish and a large black coffee. The coffee was welcome but the pastry remained untouched.

'Aren't you going to eat that?' asked Richard. She shook her head.

'Pity to waste it,' he said, reaching for the plate.

They bypassed Padua and Cremona and Brescia, and Hesta realised she couldn't carry on with the rest of this interminable journey. Now, instead of watching out for place names, she began to scan every sign for some indication of an airport. An hour or so later, to her enormous relief, as they headed towards Milan she saw a sign indicating the way to Milan airport. In a voice she could hardly recognise as her own, she said, 'I think it would be best if you drop me off here at the airport and I'll get a flight home.'

'Certainly, if that's what you want,' said Richard, ever polite and considerate, and turned off the highway to follow the signs. 'As a matter of fact I've had enough driving for one day. I'll find myself somewhere to stay tonight, preferably outside the city. Maybe an old villa or a decent inn of some sort. I'll check it out in the Good Hotel Guide.'

At the airport he handed her the laundry bag, then looked at her, probably for the first time since they'd set off.

'You don't look very happy,' he said with some surprise. 'I can't think why, after all this was all your fault, not mine or Sandra's.'

Hesta stared at him in disbelief as he climbed back into his car and drove off without a backward glance. The next flight to London was due in two hours' time. She bought a ticket she could ill afford and waited in the empty airport lounge, curled up on an uncomfortable green plastic bench with her head leaning against the cold plate-glass window overlooking the runway. She felt nothing very much. It seemed there was, after all, a limit to the amount of emotion one can feel at any one time.

Hours later Hesta was back at home with her dogs and a very surprised dog-cum-house-sitting friend. She decided to open the bottle of vintage champagne she had kept in the fridge ready for their return. It tasted pretty good, and she felt better than she had for ages.

Time, they say, is a great healer, and Hesta thought she ought to give time a chance. No one knew she was back, so she decided to leave her answering machine on and keep a low profile; she wanted to be quiet and on her own. The next evening the phone rang, and to her utter amazement it was Richard, who left a message saying he had arrived back and was planning to spend the rest of the week at his country house. He phoned her the next day and the day after that and the day after that, and Hesta couldn't understand it. What on earth did he want? And then she realised what it was. Of course! He wanted what he couldn't have. Now if only she'd been good at game-playing, Hesta might have won Richard off Sandra there and then, and for a moment she certainly was tempted. But then she remembered all the misery and hurt that had been dragging her down for so long, and although she knew there would be difficult times ahead, suddenly she felt free. Smiling to herself, she reached for the phone.

# HESTA'S LAMENT

You interviewed me on our very first date
Just as though you were hiring staff,
And you thought that as long as you told me the truth
You could use me, entire or half.
At first I suppose you decided I might
At a long shot provide what you needed
Unless the pursuing of her you were wooing
Would pay off at last and succeeded.

You clung onto me like a sailor at sea
Who's been pitched into turbulent waters,
And you thought that by giving material things
You could keep me in unloving quarters.
Yes your distance you kept, making sure that I knew
That your future belonged to another,
So I had to pretend being just a good friend
While my feelings I tried hard to smother.

Oh, you kept me on ice in your cold bed of sex
Never warming me, never a cuddle,
No, you kept your integrity, staying aloof,
Simply screwing me into a muddle.
But you'd bitten off more than you wanted to chew
When I questioned our non coalition.
So you ended the game saying I was to blame,
In that time-honoured male tradition.

# THE BEAUREGARDS

'We're having an indoor firework party on the fifth. Dean and I would love you to come, can you make it?'

It was Diane on the phone.

'Indoor fireworks?' I queried.

'Well,' she said with a laugh, 'we live in an upstairs flat, so I'm afraid we've no outside to call our own.'

Now I know about indoor fireworks. Many years ago when I was still married, one Guy Fawkes night my then husband brought home a box of indoor fireworks. It was a large, gaudy flat pack, claiming to be 'CHILDREN'S INDOOR FIREWORKS (FUN WEATHER OR NOT!)'. At the time we lived in the top flat of a converted Victorian house, so grown-up fireworks were out of the question. After dinner we spent ten minutes or so in the darkened sitting room lighting the smallest of touch papers, and, without having to stand well clear, watched the mini Catherine wheels and baby rockets flicker and fizzle out. The sparklers were the most fun, but there were only two, and after a brief effervescence left us each holding a charred wire twig. As I said, that had been a good while ago, and I could only surmise that indoor fireworks must have vastly improved to warrant an indoor display.

The couple who extended the invitation were Dean and Diane Beauregard, acquaintances rather than friends, whom I had met at a private viewing in an art gallery in Barnes. The canvases had not been to my taste, and as I wandered around the room, a glass of inferior white wine in my hand, I hoped no one would ask my opinion of what I saw. It was Dean who spoke to me as we stood side by side gazing at yet another depiction of square sheep grazing on what appeared to be a carpet of metal shavings.

'Poor little buggers,' he said, 'it must be hell on their hooves.'

'Can't do much for their digestion either,' I responded. We laughed and introduced ourselves, then decided that however poor the wine, we would need a refill if we were to continue the circuit of cubed cattle. As we headed towards the table with its quarter-filled glasses Dean pointed out a couple near the door engrossed in conversation.

'That,' he said waving a hand in their direction, 'is my wife. The tall good-looking one, I mean. The other is Phyllis Potts, our intrepid painter of morose mutton, or did you know?'

'No, I didn't,' I said, looking at them both with renewed interest. At first glance I had assumed the pair to be a man and a woman because at a distance there was nothing about Phyllis Potts that revealed her true gender. Her severely cropped hair emphasised the largeness of her nose and the square thrust of her jaw. She wore stout leather shoes, a pair of crumpled corduroy trousers, and a tight dogs-tooth jacket that had seen better days. Had it not been for the ample bosom that strained its buttons to their very limit, she could easily have been mistaken her for a stocky little man.

'As you can tell, Phyllis is in love with Diane, has been for years! Can't blame her, so have I,' Dean laughed. 'And, as you see, Diane targets the vulnerable of whatever gender. She's a tease and a very naughty girl!' Then raising his glass to me he asked: 'How about you?'

I was nonplussed. Was he asking if, like his wife, I was a tease and a naughty girl? Or, indeed, if I had bisexual tendencies? Possibly all three! Not wanting to appear in any way censorious, 'Well,' I said, 'it depends.'

'What do you mean, it depends?' he laughingly insisted.

I tried a mysterious half smile and said the first thing that came into my head.

'That's for me to know and you to find out.'

Instantly I regretted it. It wasn't a game I cared to play.

'Oh, you women!' Dean sighed heavily in mock exasperation, 'I never will understand you, thank the Lord!' And draining his glass he set off across the room.

'Come on,' he said over his shoulder, 'let me introduce you.'

As is often the way of it, I met them again unexpectedly the following week at a dinner party given by Hugh Riding, a friend of long standing who had recently landed a pithy job with a publisher, and this was by way of celebration. Hugh met me at the door, and as we entered the drawing room I caught sight of Dean, tall, wiry and bearded, with Diane at his side. He saw me and waved.

'I see you know the Beauregards,' commented my host handing me a glass of champagne off a nearby tray.

'No, not really,' I said. 'I met them briefly at Phyllis Potts's exhibition. Do you know them well?'

'Pretty well.'

'They seem an interesting couple. What... if anything... do they do for a living?' I asked. 'They're obviously connected with the arts.'

'Obviously,' Hugh agreed. 'As a matter of fact Dean is a sculptor... of limited talent, I'm afraid, but commercially useful. As for Diane, she purports to be an actress, although the sensible girl has accepted the fact that she isn't particularly good, nor indeed, particularly bad. She gets small parts from time to time, as long as it's the look that counts rather than the performance.'

'Well, no surprises there!' I said dismissively.

'Don't be too sure,' Hugh retorted, 'they're not all they seem... you want to tread carefully.'.

'What do you mean?' I asked, my curiosity aroused.

'Not now, my dear, not now,' Hugh said with his enigmatic smile. 'Off you go, I have other guests to attend to, and I see Dean is trying to attract your attention.'

I crossed the room and was greeted by Dean with a kiss on both cheeks, and an embrace from Diane that all but smothered me in the copious folds of her fringed shawl and the overwhelming musk of her perfume. She was a statuesque woman with large breasts, and the features of her pretty face were surprisingly small. She had a habit, I noticed, of throwing her head back and running her fingers through her thick, auburn hair. This gesture was, at first, mesmerising, but after a while became an irritation. At dinner Dean and I were placed beside one another, whilst Diane dispensed charm and largesse at the other end of the table; it was fascinating watching her manipulate her fellow diners. Dean never took his eyes off her, remarking at one point: 'She really is something else, don't you agree?' Indeed I did, though what that might be was a matter of opinion.

After the meal we sat over coffee and liqueurs in Hugh's spacious drawing room. Dean, by then a little drunk, was sprawled beside me on a sofa when Diane strolled over, kissed him on the forehead, and sat herself comfortably at his feet. Raising his head he smiled, closed his eyes, and began stroking her hair.

'Do you mind if I ask you something?' she asked me.

'It depends,' I said warily.

Dean opened an eye. 'Her favourite word, that, "depends". She uses it to avoid answering penetrating questions!'

'You've been asking penetrating questions, have you?' Diane asked with a laugh. 'You really are the limit!' and taking his hand she placed it firmly back in his lap and turned her attention to me.

'I was wondering,' she said, 'whether actors like you who are known for comedy, regret it. Well, I don't mean actually *regret* it,' she corrected herself, 'I just wondered if you'd like to have been given the chance to play...'

'Hamlet?' I broke in and smiled. 'Oh Diane, if you knew how often people ask me that question!'

I explained how rewarding I found it making people laugh and how comedy timing was a gift, and that although I'd never actually been offered Hamlet, I did get the chance to play straight roles from time to time. She seemed genuinely interested in what I had to say, and I was about to launch into an anecdote about a television play I'd appeared in when Dean raised himself up on an elbow.

'Never mind all that!' he said, slurring a little. 'What I want to know is, do you enjoy performing?'

'Of course I do!' I replied. 'I'd have thought that was pretty obvious.'

'But what if you were given something to do you thought you'd enjoy, and after a bit you realised you'd been wrong. What would you do?'

'Well, I'd just get on with it. I make it a rule to always finish what I've started.'

'Always?'

'Always,' I replied with mock fervour. 'Well, it would depend.'

'That's my girl!' he chortled. Then he leaned so closely towards me that I was uncomfortably aware of his alcoholic breath, and asked: 'Which parts do you like best, then? Straight? Or more diverse? Or does that also… depend?'

'Dean, that's enough!' Diane struggled to her feet. 'I don't know what's got into him,' she said with an apologetic smile, 'apart from over-indulging in Hugh's vintage cellar!' She put a hand on Dean's shoulder. 'I think you owe Sheila an apology, Dean, don't you?'

Before I could protest, Dean, sounding like a contrite schoolboy, said, 'Sorry, Sheila, sorry if I overstepped the mark. Didn't mean to. Forgive me, will you? Will you forgive me, Sheila? Please?'

Uncertain as to whether or not I was the butt of some covert joke, I gave the only response I could think of that might lighten this rather silly situation…

'Well,' I said. 'That depends.'

The three of us laughed perhaps a little too heartily, but at least it deflected what might have been an awkward end to the evening. Still, it left me with some misgivings about any future contact with the couple.

However, it seemed small-minded to turn down the invitation to their party just because of a silly social lapse, and anyway I was curious to know how they ticked, so it was with this in mind that I accepted. I was equally intrigued by the promise of indoor fireworks. My only misgiving, apart from the fact that it was a drizzly evening, was that I was filming the following day, which meant an early start and no late night. Driving through the wet streets I decided that, on the plus side, at least the night's entertainment would be held indoors.

Number thirty-four was one of a row of terraced houses, and, as instructed, I rang the top bell. Just then a man swathed in some sort of cloak bounded up the steps and pushed past me.

'Come on!' he barked, 'it's open!'

He pushed at the door which swung wide.

'Coming up?' And without waiting for a reply he grabbed my hand and raced me up several flights of stairs. We reached a landing where the door of the flat was open, the light inside bright, the music loud and upbeat. Several guests had gathered in the hallway, glasses in hand, talking animatedly. And there stood Diane looking stunning in a deep blue caftan, her cleavage low, her hair piled high.

'I didn't know you knew each other!' She had to shout to be heard.

'We don't!' replied my companion, throwing his arms around her.

'Get off me, Greg, you're all wet!'

He swung off his dripping cape, eliciting cries of dismay from those within spraying distance.

'I found this young lady at the front door and thought she'd add to the fun, so here she is!'

Diane introduced us. This was Greg, she said, an up-and-coming playwright whose first play was running to great acclaim in a small venue in Holloway. Extricating himself from a group nearby, Dean came over carrying two glasses.

'Welcome!' He kissed me on both cheeks and handed me a drink.

'Our very own brew,' he informed me proudly, 'made especially for the occasion… dynamite!'

One sip told me he wasn't wrong. I decided to carry it as a prop rather than drink it as a potion.

Others arrived, all seeming thoroughly at home as they wandered in and out of the various rooms. Trays of canapés were passed around by willing guests, glasses filled and filled again, but disappointingly I could see no sign of fireworks. Perhaps there weren't to be any after all. Perhaps they were simply using the night as an excuse for a party. But no, they had specifically said indoor fireworks. I cornered Dean.

'When are the fireworks going to start?' I asked.

'Take it easy,' he said, putting an arm around my shoulders, 'there's no hurry. Just enjoy getting to know everyone, okay?'

I was about to mention my early start but he was gone. Another half hour went by and I was getting edgy about having to leave before the display started, so I decided to have one last shot at getting things moving. This time I approached Diane, beckoning her away from her circle of friends. Explaining that I had a five a.m. start the following morning, I told her I really didn't want to miss the fun and could they possibly start the fireworks now?

'My goodness,' she said with a laugh, 'you really are keen! All right, I'll see what I can do.'

She crossed over to Dean who was deep in conversation, took him aside, and after a brief exchange he looked across at me and smiled. As they left the room and headed down the corridor I felt a thrill of anticipation. Then the lights began to dim, the music changed to slow and moody, and several cushions and rugs that I had assumed to be part of the

Beauregards' exotic decor were placed onto any available space on the floor. I watched with rising panic as clothes were slowly shed and couples began to caress and couple. I was at a loss! Taking part was out of the question, and this decision hardened (unfortunate choice of word!) when Greg the dramatist came towards me gyrating suggestively wearing nothing but a string vest. I forced a weak smile and backed away, avoiding as best I could the bodies on the floor.

'Sorry, Greg, I'd love to join in but I've got a really early start in the morning,' I burbled, 'and I don't want to start anything I can't er... finish.'

My rejection didn't seem to bother him, he simply turned around and gyrated away. I managed somehow to negotiate my way to the hall where activity seemed slightly less frenetic. As I searched out my coat and bag from the jumble on the hat stand and reached for the handle of the front door, I heard someone call my name. I turned, and there stood Dean. He seemed to be wearing Diane's caftan. It was wide open down the front, displaying his naked torso, his bare, surprisingly spindly legs, and his manhood, erect and ready for action.

'You're not leaving us, are you?' He approached slowly. 'You can't do that, darling, particularly as it was you who got things started. And I seem to remember you saying you always finished what you started!'

Carefully replacing things onto the hat stand, I walked towards him, slowly unbuttoning my blouse. His eyes narrowed. He licked his upper lip with the tip of his tongue.

'Oh, baby,' he murmured.

I put my arms around his neck, and close to his ear whispered, 'Okay, I'll risk it if you will. And there's no need to worry, it's only a herpes and I'm on antibiotics.'

Next morning I was up fresh and early and ready for work. Amazing what an early night can do for a girl.

# MISSING THE BASTARD

He's gone away
Hoorah Hooray
My time's my own
All night all day
A week of this
What utter bliss
I'm free
Whoopee.
I think I'll go
And see a show
Who shall I ask
Well, how 'bout Mo
Or Sue or Jean
No, I'm not keen.
Oh blow
Won't go.

I miss the rows
The knotted brows
The passions only
He can rouse
It's daft I know
But there you go.
Too late.
My Fate

But oh, the thought
That I've been caught
The sex war won
The battle fought
Still, time has taught
I sought and fought
The sort
I ought.

# A BASTARD PROFESSION

I'm an invisible mender
Of the feminine gender
My plight you may find hard to understand.
I've overdone my concentration,
Too much sense of my vocation,
And the situation's getting out of hand.
I love my work so dearly
It's affecting me quite clearly
And I'm fading, disappearing out of sight.
My face is getting faceless
And the jokes can get quite tasteless
Like 'Stop using so much vanishing cream at night'.

I sit inside this window every morning
And people stop, admiring as they pause,
I feel like some great actress
When I work on this or that dress
All that's missing is the thunderous applause.
I get so enthusiastic
About hiding some elastic,
And though some may find this sewing job a bore
I love patching worn out places
Leaving nothing of the traces
Of the places where the traces were before.

Is it me, or can you see what is occurring?
Is my outline slightly fuzzy in your eyes?
I don't think I'm going crazy
But my memory's getting hazy
And I think I just might dematerialise.
Still, I'll stick with my profession
Without making an impression
Even though it seems a hefty price to pay.
Still, there's one thought keeps me going
As invisibly I'm sewing…
I'll never die, I'll only fade away.

# EFFIE

I can't think why I agreed to go in the first place. I don't like new places, they make me feel insecure, and I don't like eating foreign food because I've got a stomach. I'm not a well woman, never have been. It runs in the family. Not my mother, though, my mother was well all her life. Until she died. But my grandmother wasn't well. They say inheritages skip a generation so that probably accounts for it. Still, it's nice to feel well even if you're not healthy and that's what I try to do.

I've known Ron and Cynthia ever since, oh, ages ago. Got to know them at the synagogue, as you do. If you're Jewish, that is. Matter of fact Ron used to play gin rummy with my ex fiancé Stanley. When I say fiancé, it never actually came to that. Almost but not quite. Lasted for ten years on and off, and then off. Anyway, back to the Berkowitzes, Ron and Cynthia to you. About eight months ago they decided to up sticks and migrate to Israel. At their age, I ask you! Brave, especially as she was under the doctor. And him, too. They were neither of them well from time to time. Not like me, my health is permanent. Anyway, last month I received this really generous invitation to visit them as their guest in their new homeland of Tel Aviv, all expenses paid. Apart of course from spending money, which was fine by me because I don't spend much. I do sometimes buy what I suppose you'd call trinkets to take home in case I ever have to give someone something for an occasion of some sort. As a matter of fact I've got quite a little hoard. Anyway, rashly I wrote back and accepted and then realised what I'd done. I hate airports and I'm no good at travelling. But then I thought no, you've said you'll go, and you don't want to disappoint them.

The journey started the way things usually start for me, badly. The flight to Israel dictated I should leave the house by five a.m. in order to get to the car park somewhere near the airport that Ron had helped me book. I'm never much good at getting up, let alone getting up early, so I was already running late when I slammed the front door behind me and then realised I'd left the hall light on. As I fumbled through my handbag for the door keys, my wheelie case tipped over and clattered down the steps, landing rocking on its side. Anyway I sorted the 'light out' (Joke!) and there was no damage done to the case, but after a night of freezing temperatures the car refused to start. Eventually the engine caught, and as it warmed up I sprinted around spraying the windows with de-icing fluid, only to find I had nothing to wipe the windows clean with. I sat huddled in the driver's seat watching the liquid run down until I could use the windscreen wipers. It was dark, it was cold, and just for a moment I began to regret accepting my friends' invitation, but I pulled myself together, and smoothing out the paper printed with instructions of how to get to the car park, placed it carefully on the passenger seat beside me and set off.

I do drive. As a matter of fact I drive quite well although I'm possibly a little on the slow side, which can sometimes annoy other drivers. Still, I won't be bullied into breaking the law. The instructions specified that in order to catch my flight, the car had to be in the car park by six a.m. and it wasn't long before I began to worry that I might have underestimated the amount of time I had to get there. I cautiously picked up speed, and was doing pretty well when I almost ran into the back of the car ahead of me and had to brake sharply. As I did so the paper along with my handbag slid to the floor, and when I tried to reach them my seat belt held me back. Should I waste precious time pulling over and stopping? I decided I could remember the directions, so on I sped until I came to a big roundabout where the signs were so confusing, I had to drive around it several times trying to decide which exit to take. Beginning to panic I stopped, only to find I had pulled up on the wrong side of the roundabout facing the opposite way. Retrieving the piece of paper, I perused it with difficulty by the light on the dashboard, but the instructions weren't clear, so, finding a telephone number at the bottom of the page, I shook my bag out onto the seat beside me, found my mobile and dialled the number. An automated person informed me he was sorry but the office was closed and would be open again at eight a.m! How ridiculous! There was nothing for it. I got out in the dawn light clutching the piece of paper, and when a car finally drove by, I waved at it and the driver accelerated away. The second car gave me a wide berth, and the next two ignored me. By now I was near to tears, shivering with cold, and had to stamp my feet to keep them from going numb. Taking my life into my hands I stood in the middle of the road, and when a small van approached I waved my arms above my head. The driver pulled up... he had no choice, really... and winding down his window shouted something equivalent to *That's a silly thing to do.* Then he seemed to notice how upset I was and asked if I was in trouble. I flapped the paper at him and asked if he happened to know how to get to this car park and to my huge relief he said yes he did and he was going that way and I should follow him. I was so overwhelmed with gratitude I put my hand through his window, and grabbing the sleeve of his worn leather coat heard myself say, 'I love you! I love you!' I know it's ridiculous but that's exactly what I said. (And I meant it.)

I turned round and followed him, and when we came to a junction he waved and pointed, so I followed his point and there it was, the car park. I saw a small prefabricated building that looked like an office, so I parked nearby and struggled my case to the ground, but when I tried to pick it up my fingers refused to work. What is more, my teeth were chattering and I was barely able to speak, so leaving the case where it was I went in. The clerk, a balding man of indeterminate years, took down my details and then pushed the agreement over for me to sign, but the pen eluded my grip. He didn't seem too bothered and signed it for me.

'Just make a mark here,' he told me, so I did. Then he pointed to a single-decker bus standing outside on the tarmac. 'That's it,' he said, 'the bus.'

The driver was sitting in it with his feet up on the dashboard and a paper cup in his hand. When I tapped on his window and pointed to my case on the ground beside my car he opened his door just enough to speak through the gap.

'That your case?'

I resisted making some cutting remark and just said 'Yes,' with what I hoped was an expectant smile.

'Better get it then,' was his response.

As I dragged it painfully through the door he started up the engine and shouted, 'Hurry up, lady, or you'll blame me for missing your effing flight.'

Then he slammed the door behind me and accelerated away with a jerk that threw me backwards into a seat which happened to be occupied by the only other passenger on board. Apologising profusely, I extricated myself from his person and hauled myself onto the seat beside him. He was a chunky man in his middle age with an untidy thatch of thinning hair and wearing a cagoule. He smiled sympathetically, then pulled a wry face in the direction of the driver. I'm not keen on talking to strangers but I felt I ought to say something; after all we'd just had a 'close encounter of the first kind' (Joke!). So I asked him whither he was bound. California, he told me, to see his sister whom he hadn't seen for ten years! I didn't ask why it had been so long because it would have meant him telling me, and frankly I wasn't exactly in a listening mood. He asked me politely about my trip, and I explained it was my first trip to Israel, and the first holiday I had taken in ages. Just then his mobile rang, and as he answered I remembered with a real shock that I'd left my own phone on the passenger seat of my car, lying there for all to see and steal! My heart started to palpitate, but I'd come well prepared, and retrieving my Little Box of Allsorts (as I call it) from my bag, I swallowed one of my trusty pills (pink for palpitations). Then I got up and swayed my way forward to the driver and asked if he could retrieve my phone when he returned to base and bring it to me on his next trip back to the airport.

'What time's your flight?' he asked.

Eight thirty-five I told him, whereupon he smiled broadly and said he wouldn't be returning till nine. I asked if, in that case, he would be kind enough to retrieve the phone and keep it secure for me until my return. He sucked his teeth, shrugged his shoulders, and wobbled his head from side to side and I had absolutely no idea what he meant, and decided I would just have to abandon any thought of ever being reconciled with my phone again.

At Heathrow I queued for an age in the wrong queue, and when I'd got into the right queue it was even longer and slower. Now, I don't mind flying once the aeroplane is safely in the skies, but I do get really paranoid about the taking off and the landing. However, a very good friend of mine I used to know taught me a little trick that really takes your mind off the horrors that may occur during those crucial times and I'd be happy to share it with anyone who suffers similar anxieties. Once you've secured your safety belt, place the forefinger of your left hand just inside the metal buckle, and as the plane takes off, squeeze the buckle with the fingers of your right hand as hard as you can. The pain concentrates the mind wonderfully, but be careful not to overdo it. I did once, and spent the rest of the flight with my left forefinger held rigid in a plastic glass of iced water.

And so to Ben Gurion airport, where, once the formalities were over, I emerged unscathed from customs looking forward to being welcomed into the open arms of my host and hostess. But nothing, or rather, no one! I could feel a panic attack coming on, but I managed to hold it down and wheeled the trolley with my luggage around the circle of potted bushes, waiting to be recognised. No one showed the slightest interest in me, so I decided the only thing to do was to go back into customs and emerge once more. This I did, but still nothing and nobody. What to do now? I had been given their home phone number but my mobile was back in London, so I decided perhaps I could send out a call for them if there was a tannoy system. Going over to a likely-looking desk I tried to explain to the man what I needed but he was deliberately exasperating.

'Annoy? Why you annoy? You annoy for your friends?'

After several attempts to make myself clear I realised I was getting nowhere, when a man wearing a badge saying TAXI approached me.

'You want taxi?'

'You speak English?'

'Little,' he said, so I said no, I didn't want a taxi, I wanted a telephone, and tried to explained how I'd left my mobile in London and needed to call the people who were supposed to meet me.

'I have mobile. Give me number. I make call,' he said.

I thanked him but said I only had English notes and would need to get some change to pay him for the use of his mobile, and to make it clear I took a ten-pound note out of my purse and waved it at him.

'I make call,' he said with a dismissive wave, 'no charge.'

I fished the number out of my bag and read it out as he dialled and then handed his phone over to me. Cynthia was clearly very surprised.

'But Ron left over an hour ago!' she told me. 'He's got Fran with him… she's our other house guest. Whereabouts are you standing?'

I looked around and gave as good a description of my immediate surroundings as I could.

'Okay,' she said, 'don't move, I'll call him.'

I handed the phone back to the man and thanked him, waving the note at him again with an apologetic smile. He smiled, took the note, and left.

After what seemed an eternity I saw Ron coming towards me accompanied by a woman with bright red hair. I took an instant dislike to her (I have an instinct about these things). There were lots of hello's and how on earth did we miss you's, and then the woman, Fran, said she was sure she'd seen me but Ron said it couldn't have been me because I would have been coming out of customs and the woman she saw was going into customs. Then he said to Fran, anyway, how could you have seen her (me) as she (Fran) had never met her (me) before, and she said to Ron you told me (Fran) that Effie (me) always feels the cold, even when it's not, and I saw this woman all hunched up and just knew it was her. (It seemed my instinct was correct.)

'Can we get going?' I suggested. 'It's been a stressful time and I really do need to rest a bit.' Ron took my trolley and I followed a few paces behind them as their silly argument droned on.

Ron's car was a small two-door job, and I waited, hoping Fran would climb into the back but she waved me in, saying I'd be more comfortable because I'd have more room. I didn't tell her I get car-sick sitting in the back so I struggled in, only to have Ron heave my suitcase in beside me. More room, my eye! Fran settled herself beside Ron and proceeded to guide him out of the car park, reading out the signs we could all see perfectly well. After a bit she turned round to me and said, 'I've been to visit Ron and Cynthia before, you know.'

'Really? When was that?' I tried to sound interested, but apart from anything else I could barely move and my head was beginning to throb.

'Two thousand and… when was it, Ron?'

'Six,' he said, his eyes firmly fixed on the road ahead.

'Seven,' said Fran.

'No, six.'

Fran clicked her tongue in exasperation.

'I *came* in six,' she said, 'but I spent Christmas and New Year here, and I *left* in seven.'

Ron remained silent but a bulging muscle in his jaw spoke volumes. I think Fran must have sensed his irritation, because she added, 'So we're both right!'

We seemed to have been driving for ages and I was beginning to feel a bit nauseous. I asked where we were.

'The airport,' said Ron.

We drove on in uncomfortable silence. I was feeling too ill to start any conversation and couldn't reach my handbag for a pill, so I decided I ought to make an effort and asked Ron again where we were. It was Fran who replied.

'I know where we are,' she said, 'this is... oh, where is it again, Ron?'

'Still the airport,' he said. That shut her up, but not for long.

'This time I came over to stay with Ron and Cynthia for just a week,' she told me. 'That was ten days ago...'

'And she's still here!' said Ron, and I thought I detected a trace of bitterness in his voice.

'I'm afraid Fran's got your room,' he continued.

'Oh Ron, you should have said!' cried Fran, 'I would have changed my dates back again.'

'No, no, don't be silly,' Ron replied with admirable restraint, 'I'm sure Effie won't mind staying in the box room for the next day or... two?' The question... for I'm sure that's what it was... hung in the air, but Fran didn't seem to notice and pointed up at a billboard.

'Colgate toothpaste in Israel,' she said, 'I wonder if it has to be kosher?'

And she chortled at what I suppose she thought was a joke.

Eventually we got to the small block of flats where Ron and Cynthia now live, but by the time we arrived I was feeling distinctly under the weather. Ron had to help me up the stairs and into the flat and I could barely take in my surroundings. Cynthia, bless her, had prepared supper for us, but all I really wanted was to get my head down, so I asked for a cup of hot water, my favourite tipple, and sat on the sofa swallowing down some much needed pills (capsules for calming). In spite of it being early evening, I knew that unless I rested soon I'd be useless in the morning, so Ron took my case up the short flight of stairs at the back of their kitchen-diner to my accommodation.

The box room was full of packing cases and household bric-a-brac which my hosts had kindly cleared to one side. On the other side stood a narrow bed with a small table next to it on which stood a lamp, a carafe of water with a glass, and a little vase of welcoming flowers that sadly were wilting, probably, from the lack of light, as the skylight in the sloping ceiling was small, and the bulb in the suspended paper lantern was on the weak side. I was just beginning to wonder about the toilet facilities when Ron pointed to what I thought was a cupboard.

'That,' he told me, 'is a hidden recess with a lavvie and a wash basin in it. The people we bought the place from had them put in so that they didn't have to trudge down the stairs whenever they got caught short. So you have all the mod cons except for a shower. You'll have to use our bathroom for that. We'll probably have to form a queue!' Oh how we laughed. He left, saying, 'I'll leave you to it. Call if you need anything, and it's lovely to have you here.' He was half way down the stairs when he called out that he'd forgotten to mention there wasn't any hot water up there but that it shouldn't matter too much, and wished me happy dreams.

Well, I certainly dreamt, although it was more of a nightmare. I dreamt something was sitting on my chest, some sort of animal, and it was making this awful braying noise and it woke me up. It was me wheezing, I absolutely couldn't breathe! I turned on the bedside lamp and managed to find an appropriate pill in my Little B. of A. but had to sit bolt upright for the rest of the night. I wondered if the cause was the packet of biscuits I'd brought as a gift for Ron and Cynthia that I'd eaten before I climbed into bed, but decided it was something more serious than that.

It was Fran who pounded up the stairs the next morning shouting, 'The bathroom's free if you want a shower!' and then disappeared.

I'd unpacked a few bits and pieces the night before including my dressing gown and slippers, so I put them on and made my way downstairs feeling very frail. Ron, Cynthia and Fran were sitting at the table having breakfast.

'You must be starving!' said Cynthia after all the good mornings were over, and truth to tell I did feel a bit peckish.

'What would you like first?' she continued, 'breakfast or a shower?'

'Oh,' I said, 'I don't mind. Whatever suits you best.'

'No, Effie, you're the guest,' she said. 'The bathroom's free and breakfast will keep, so it's entirely up to you.'

Now I hate having to make decisions that don't matter. I mean if it's a matter of life and death, like whether to phone the police first or pick someone up off the floor, I'm there, because it matters. Also I don't like showers. I prefer lying in a bath having a nice long soak. Add to that the fact that I'd been up half the night and still felt breathless, you can understand why I just stood there looking indecisive. It was Fran who broke the silence.

'For Christ's sake sit down and get some food down you. You look bloody awful,' she said through a mouthful of muesli.

Honestly, I had to look away! I can't stand it when people talk with their mouths full. I was grateful to her for coming to my rescue, but she really is crass. That's the word, crass. Anyway, I sat down and had a few rounds of toast, two eggs (over-boiled... I like them runny) and a cup of hot water with a tea bag and some milk in it, just for a change. Cynthia insisted I have a piece of melon, and when she asked me why I'd only eaten the top layer I told her that I'd heard the flesh of the melon nearest the skin was toxic and I have a very sensitive stomach. Fran choked on her coffee and yelped, 'Crap!' Like I said, crass.

The three of them were going off to the local market to do some shopping, but I declined to join them and headed off to the bathroom. Wouldn't you know it, there wasn't a bath in it, only a glass shower cubicle. Just as well I hadn't mentioned my preference! I had a quick douse, and, having dressed, spent the morning sitting on the sofa watching an American news channel and feeling fragile. The sofa was leather and the seat sloped forwards so I kept sliding off it. However, I found that if I held onto the back and sat sideways with my feet up, I could stay more or less put. They returned at lunchtime with some bottles and bags of food, and Cynthia started getting lunch ready while Fran set the table and Ron went to check his emails. I told Cynthia not to cook anything for me but she said, 'Don't be silly, you must eat, and anyway it's only cold stuff, salads and things,' which shook me, because I know for a fact that you should never eat salad things in hot foreign countries and only drink bottled water. I didn't like to say anything though, so I bit my lip and told myself, Effie, you are just going to have to risk it and pray.

After lunch I felt quite bloated. I'm not used to eating large amounts in the middle of the day so I thought I'd have a siesta, and stretched out again on the sofa, not realising it was where Cynthia usually puts her feet up after lunch. Ron mentioned it, but she insisted I stay where I was, and went to lie down in their bedroom, while Ron settled into 'his' armchair with his feet up on a stool thing and Fran sat at the table reading a book. I must have dozed off because I was woken by Fran shaking me.

'You're wheezing like an old camel!' she said.

I apologised and said I couldn't help it, I wasn't well, and she said something like what you need is a brisk walk and some fresh air. Little does she know either of those would certainly exacerbate my health but I said nothing and closed my eyes. I was woken again with a start by the sound of a book slamming down and a chair scraping along the floor. It was Fran.

'For Chrissake!' she yelled as she headed towards the door, referring to me once more in hurtful animal terms. I looked over to where Ron was but he'd abandoned his chair and gone elsewhere.

I won't burden you with details of the rest of the day spent on my own in the flat, nor with the misery of my second night in the box room. Suffice it to say that at one point Fran came up and shook me awake saying, 'Your wheezing and snoring is thundering through the whole apartment. You're rattling the ornaments!'

I was really upset but what was I to do? Sit up again and try to keep myself awake all night? I decided that even though this was a holiday I would have to take time out to see a doctor. I'd ask Ron about it in the morning, and with that small crumb of comfort I pulled the pillow over my head and hoped I wouldn't die of suffocation.

Ron and Cynthia's doctor's surgery was mercifully only a short drive from the flat, and as I sat in the waiting room with Ron at my side I began to feel a little more myself. Ron didn't speak much, he seemed a little out of sorts and I wondered if I should mention his condition to the doctor, but decided against it. After all, he's a grown man. As for my consultation, the doctor, an Israel person, could not have been more charming or sympathetic. I told him how I couldn't breathe and how I had thought I was dying, and he felt my pulse and then asked me to lie down on his couch and relax. Then he examined my chests. There was something about the way he examined them that made me feel confident he understood my problems. He tapped my abdomen and listened to my heart, and then he said just turn on your side and lie quiet for a few minutes and in a while I think you'll find you can breathe normally. If it happens again, he said, lie on your side, not your back. It's all a matter of position, is what he said. Well, I left feeling much better, so that's what I shall do in future.

On the way back I thanked Ron for so generously paying the doctor's bill, and he said if his advice works it'll be worth every penny. Wasn't that nice of him? In fact it made me feel so close to him I decided to confide in him. I told him that I often get wheezy when I feel anxious. He seemed a little put out by this, and asked why I hadn't mentioned this before. Well, I told him, the reason I'd become anxious was that I was anxious that if I told him I get anxious it would have made him anxious, and that would only have made me wheeze even more, and the last thing I wanted was for him to feel anxious about me. This must have set his mind at rest, although I noticed he was gripping the steering wheel and his knuckles were quite white, poor lamb. Perhaps I should have mentioned something to the doctor after all.

That night I slept passably well on my side (blessings on that nice medic!) although from time to time the odd snort woke me and I'd find I was lying on my back, but at least there were no stampedes from Madam. After breakfast and a quick shower of my extremities, it was suggested we all go to a market place to look at the stalls with their exotic wares like carpets and trinkets and such. I hate crowds and I'm susceptible to the heat, but Cynthia kindly loaned me an old straw hat of hers, for which I was grateful even though it smelled of hay, and although the sun was blazing I kept my cardigan on to avoid my arms getting burnt. Fran was in a very jolly mood. She'd brought a bottle of water with her and I must say I did wish I'd thought of bringing one too. I wasn't planning to shop much. The only person I'd decided to take a gift back for was my Pilipino cleaner Gracie, and I mentioned this to Fran in passing. We were walking down an alley full of carpets and sandals and men in frocks inviting us in for coffee, when we saw one stall in particular that was crammed with all sorts of everythings. Fran took me by the arm and marched me in, telling Ron and Cynthia we'd meet them later at a certain café in the square.

There was such a selection I couldn't make up my mind about what to buy and Fran was no help. Every time I picked up something to look at, she would say, 'Oh that's lovely!' or 'Haven't you got good taste!' And so on. She followed me round collecting up all the things I'd been looking at, I thought to be helpful so that I could make my mind up as to what to choose for Gracie. Instead Fran turned to the Arab stall owner (whom, I may say, she'd been flirting with ever since we'd walked in), and said: 'How much for the lot?' I tried to explain I only wanted one item but neither of them took any notice of me. They had this banter back and forth in either Hebrew or Arabic or possibly both, with lots of hand gestures, which ended up with Fran saying to me (in English), 'You lucky so-and-so, that's quite a bargain!' By then he'd wrapped them all up together and Fran told me he'd agreed to take traveller's cheques worth fifteen pounds for the lot and I'd be a fool to miss such an amazing deal. I only had ten pounds' worth with me (nearly all the allowance I'd permitted myself), but Fran whipped out her purse and said, 'You can owe me five!' As we were leaving, the stall owner kissed her hand and gave her his blessing several times over and she raised her bottle of water to him and took a swig and they laughed a lot. So there I was with a parcel of things I didn't want… in fact I didn't even remember what I'd paid for! Later I asked Cynthia if Fran was always that exuberant.

'Oh yes,' she said, 'as long as she's got her bottle with her, she's exuberant all right,' and she gave me a funny look that could only have meant one thing! Who'd have thought it! Mind you, I did notice her breath smelt a bit funny close up, but I assumed it was all that foreign Israeli food she'd been consuming.

Back at the flat I found I'd bought two long strands of beads, a little iron terrapin whose shell lifted up to reveal an ashtray, a bronze saucer with a few words in Hebrew or possibly Arabic etched on it, a pair of heavy silver earrings that I'm sure I hadn't picked out and that would have stretched your earlobes with their weight, and a filigree bracelet that I must confess I quite liked. I thought I might keep it for myself, but when I tried it on it slipped right off my hand. I don't know if Gracie smokes, and I don't think she's one for jewellery, so I think I'll play it safe and give her the saucer; I'm sure she'll find several uses for it. After a lie down that I really needed plus a few remedial pills I staggered downstairs. It was six o'clock and Ron said he was going to take us all out for dinner to a stall that had the best 'falafel' in Tel Aviv. I wasn't over-keen but didn't want to play 'wet blanket', so I said nothing. Cynthia and I sat in the back of the car. She was behind Ron and kept leaning forward to tell him which way to go and he kept saying 'All right dear' and not following her instructions. She was obviously used to this because she said things like, 'God, you're always so stubborn,' or 'You never listen, do you?' Then as we were driving past a sort of monument with a wide flight of shallow steps in front of it (which admittedly could have been mistaken for a road), Cynthia said turn right, and for the first time Ron did what she said and drove right up the steps! Cynthia shouted, 'No, later!' But it was too late. Several tourists jumped out of the way and one man shook his fist at us and swore. Ron stopped at the top in front of some pillars, and when I looked out of my window there was a sheer drop! Nobody said anything, not even Cynthia; I think we were all in shock. I just shut my eyes tight while Ron finally managed to turn the car around in the minimal space, and as we bumped our way back down the steps I had a funny feeling Ron had done it on purpose.

We parked in a side street off a busy main road full of very ordinary-looking shops, and followed Ron to one of several food stands lined up on the pavement.

'This man,' said Ron, greeting a bearded man in a chef's hat, who was standing behind the counter of one of them, as an old friend. 'This man,' he repeated, 'makes the finest falafels in Tel Aviv!'

He ordered without asking what we wanted, saying, 'I know the best combination, trust me.'

There was nowhere to sit, so I leaned against a car parked at the side, and hoped the driver wouldn't turn up. Soon we were holding these giant sort of pastry envelopes filled with I dared not ask what, but I could tell the vegetables were pickled, and what I think was meat was doused in a very spicy sauce. Now I can't eat spicy foods; I've got what they call a geographic tongue, which means I can only eat European foods. But there I was, stood there holding onto this unwieldy falafel. Ron waited excitedly for our approval, so there was nothing for it but to get it down, knowing I would rue the consequences later.

And of course there *were* consequences. I was laid low for the whole of the next day, lying there in my little box room with my Little Box of Allsorts to hand, while Cynthia very kindly brought me up trays. Later when I felt up to it I sat downstairs in front of the television gripping the back of the sofa. I found an old copy of the *Daily Mail* and tried to do the crossword but it eluded me. They say doing crosswords is good for your mind, but it's not true. I knew someone who did crosswords all his life and he got Alzheimer's. In the evening as we sat round the table after Cynthia had persuaded me to join them for a simple supper, Fran mentioned she planned to go on a coach trip to the Dead Sea the following day. She had a brochure which I asked to look at, and it certainly seemed interesting. Then I noticed something in the blurb that bothered me. It said that the Dead Sea was four hundred metres below sea level. Now I go deaf when going downhill, but Fran reassured me, saying it was probably a slow descent and I'd acclimatise as we went down, so I took a big deep breath and asked if I could join her.

The following morning Ron drove us to a hotel forecourt and we climbed onto the waiting coach, which to my surprise and delight was absolutely empty.

I said, 'It looks like we're the only people going! We'll have the whole coach to ourselves!'

Fran said, 'Don't be idiotic. This is the first pick-up point and we just happen to be the first on.' Sure enough at the next stop several people were waiting, and as they boarded the coach I noticed a group of Israeli teenagers piling into a bus nearby. There were girls as well as boys all wearing khaki uniforms and carrying rifles! What's more, they were all chewing gum! In uniform, I ask you! When I was at school we'd have been severely reprimanded if we'd been caught chewing gum in our school uniforms. I didn't say anything to Fran, she'd only have made some clever riposte. We made a few more stops and the coach filled up completely. One thing that struck me was that everyone in Israel seems to be Jewish. But not the Arabs, of course. I was beginning to feel a bit claustrophobic so I reached into my bag for my L. B. of A. and was devastated to find I'd left it on the bedside table! There was nothing I could do about it so I leaned my head against the window and kept my eyes closed till Fran shook me and said we'd stopped to look at a view. We were parked at the top of the ruins of an old Roman fort, and Fran insisted I get out. I'm glad I did because it was quite stunning. We stood there, around us the massive carved stones worn away by time and the wind, ahead of us the vast biblical panorama with the Dead Sea in the distance. The sense of the depth of history and the battle of the elements washed over me, and, filled with a sense of wonder, I turned to Fran and said: 'They ought to build a hotel here.' I could tell by the way she looked at me she was struggling for words, so she must have felt much the same as I did.

Later we stopped at a wayside café which had a souvenir shop attached. I didn't bother to look in it, I'd already done my shopping (thanks to Madam!) but I was feeling a bit peckish, and although the set lunch looked a bit hefty, the cost was included in the ticket so it seemed silly to look a gift horse in the mouth. (Joke!) After lunch on we sped, and I won't bore you with the bits of history the driver pointed out. Truth to tell the microphone system hurt my head, and what with my ear problem I wasn't an altogether happy bunny. But then came the unforgettable experience of The Dead Sea Spa.

We alighted off the coach... Fran had brought her swimsuit with her, and although she'd suggested I do the same I hadn't because I don't swim much, and frankly I don't feel comfortable exposing my body to scrutiny. Not that there's anything wrong with my body; one way and another I'm quite satisfied with it. Everyone seemed quite excited about the Dead Sea Experience and I began to regret my lack of equipment, so, even though I'm squeamish about wearing other people's intimates, I joined the queue for hiring swimming attire. When I got to the desk a woman with a foreign accent asked me what size I was in English, and then handed me a towel, a sort of shower cap, some rubber flip flops, and a swimsuit with quite distinctive blue and white stripes. I noticed the two women in front of me had been handed exactly the same, so I deduced it was some sort of uniform in case anyone decided to make off with their property. Highly unlikely! I followed the others into the changing room with some trepidation, but it was too late to change my mind so I changed my clothes instead! (Joke!) I locked my belongings in a locker with a key that was attached to a large sort of safety pin, I guessed so that you could pin it on yourself, thus avoiding having to carry it in your hand. It came in very handy when one of the swimsuit's straps kept slipping off my shoulder and I used it to shorten it a bit. The flip flops were never better named... I flip-flopped all over the place! I've no idea how people put up with having a thong between their toes. Still, it was marginally better than sand, which irritates my feet and brings me out in a rash. I decided the shower cap would at least keep the sun off my head, so I pulled it on and put the towel around my shoulders as a protective cape.

As I left the changing room I saw Fran walking out of the reception area and down some wooden steps onto the beach, and scuttled after her as best I could. She informed me that she was going to take a mud bath, which of course is one of the very main reasons for visiting the spa in the first place because it's chock full of vitamins and healing powers. As I struggled to keep up with her she pointed out a small open tram on rails and suggested I might find that an easier option. As I climbed on, the man at the front who had his back to me clanged a bell and it set off with a jerk. There was no one else on it, and I had just settled on one of the wooden benches when it pulled up beside a queue of people who had obviously all been swimming, and in they piled. Everyone was speaking in foreign tongues, and I found myself squeezed between a large wet (I think German) woman, and another woman who began drying her hair vigorously, digging her elbow into me as she did so. The bell clanged, the tram did a semicircle, and then headed back to the place where I'd got on! Everyone alighted so I alighted too and wondered what on earth was going on! I must have looked confused, because a nice man came up to me.

'I see you English,' he said, looking at me with what looked like pity, 'You have problem?'

I explained that I had wanted to go down to the sea in the tram thing, but it had brought me back instead.

'Ah,' he said with a laugh and pointed. 'That side you go, this side you come back!'

So that was it! Simple when you know how.

And soon I was standing on the edge of the Dead Sea, with the Dead Sea spread out in front of me. I caught sight of several people covered in the black mud standing and, I assumed, drying off. Nearby were two large barrels filled with the stuff, and there was a man actually standing inside a third barrel smoothing it over his person. Then I recognised Fran's unmistakeable extremely red hair on one of the mud-covered figures, and when I reached her she said stiffly through the mud on her face, 'You want to get yourself some of this, it'll tone up your pasty skin!' Ignoring her observation I asked how one removed the mud afterwards. She pointed to what looked like a shallow paddling pool with several showers in the centre.

'Get going!' she urged. 'You'll regret it if you don't!'

I decided to risk it. I went over to one of the unmanned barrels (Joke!) and, keeping my flip flops on, scooped up the mud with my hands and covered my legs almost up to my knees and my arms up to my elbows – I figured those extremities would be the easiest to clean off. (Did I mention I don't like showers?) The mud was smooth and warm and I must say rather pleasant. It smelled, surprisingly, rather earthy with just a touch of the sea. I stood in the sun with my arms out horizontally waiting for the mud to dry but being careful to keep the towel over my shoulders. However, after a while I got a bit restless, so I headed for the showers where I managed to wash the mud off by using the water in the paddling pool. Fran appeared just as I was drying myself off and remarked: 'Well, having survived that you better get yourself into the sea.'

Assuming no one would be interested in purloining my towel or flip flops, I left them in a tidy pile a few feet from the gently lapping waves, and walked slowly towards My Dead Sea Experience. I was surprised that there were only a few other people bathing. There was a fat man floating on his back with his eyes closed, oblivious to the world; there were two women at the deeper end jabbering away in what sounded like Hebrew, and a young girl in her teens who seemed to be in a trance. An area of the sea had been cordoned off by a thick rope suspended on large yellow balls The water was surprisingly calm and pleasantly cool, and when the water reached my chests I decided that was as deep as I wanted to go. I put my arms in front of me to have a gentle paddle and, pushing myself forwards, lifted my legs. And that was my big mistake, because I was now face down in the water, and the salt content refused to let me change position! I could neither turn over nor stand up! So *that's* why the fat man was floating on his back! They say it's impossible to drown in the Dead Sea, and there I was, about to prove them wrong! They should have at least put up a notice. Anyway, my legs were flailing about uselessly and it was perfectly clear that I was drowning. I have no idea how long I struggled but at last, at last terrified and gasping for breath I managed to stand up. And as if all that wasn't bad enough, the strap of my bathing suit had slipped off, exposing one of my chests! The others in the water were glaring at me as, exhausted and close to tears, I dragged myself back to the safety of the beach. I picked up my things and saw Fran a little way off sunning herself, and wondered if she'd witnessed my near drowning.

'Been in I see,' she said, noticing my state of wetness. 'How was it?'

'Terrifying,' I replied. 'I nearly drowned!'

Madam threw back her head and roared with laughter.

'Only you, Effie, it could only happen to you!' she gasped when she'd recovered her breath, adding, 'You'd better go and shower all that salt off before you turn into Lot's wife.'

I staggered to the showers and forced myself to have a good dousing, saying to myself, 'Effie, you're lucky to still be alive!' When the coach was about to depart it became clear that Fran was missing, but just as the driver was about to go and search for her, she appeared running towards us and climbed aboard with a merry 'Right, off we go, then!' and no sign of an apology. As the coach accelerated away I leaned back and closed my eyes, thinking what a relief it was that Fran wasn't sitting beside me. I wasn't in the mood for her.

So that was my Big Adventure, my never-to-be-forgotten Dead Sea Experience which laid me low for the whole of the next day. Dear Cynthia assured me she didn't mind bringing trays of food up to me, but eventually I began to feel a bit guilty, so I suggested I could spend the afternoon downstairs on the sofa with my feet up, watching telly. That evening Fran suggested to Ron and Cynthia that the three of them spend the next day driving round the coast, sightseeing. They didn't ask if I wanted to join them, although I was beginning to feel a lot better and might have said yes if they had. Still, perhaps it was for the best. When I got up next morning I found they'd already left, and Cynthia had written a note telling me to help myself to anything in the fridge. I had a light breakfast and then wandered around the flat looking at things of interest. (This is a very good way to get to know people who you know more intimately.) There was nothing particularly exciting, so I sat on the balcony until the sun got too hot and went back in to watch television. I tried to change channels, but all I managed to do was end up with a screen full of snow. At midday, feeling a little peckish, I found what looked like a tart of some sort in the fridge, so I heated myself some nice hot water, dunked a tea bag and a little milk in it, and picked up an old magazine I found lying under some onions in the vegetable rack. I was so absorbed in this interesting article about a woman and her sexually deviant husband, that without realising it I consumed the entire tart! Still, Cynthia did say help yourself.

I was fast asleep on the sofa when the three of them burst in laughing and joking. As far as I could tell they were all a little the worse for wear, if you know what I mean, especially Ron, and he'd been driving! They clattered about unpacking a takeaway meal which I must confess looked quite appetising. Cynthia said they'd thought of including me but decided it was safer not to because of my stomach and my tongue. Then she said, 'Do come and join us at the table. There's a quiche in the fridge if you fancy a slice.' I declined her offer, deciding to say nothing, and hoping she wouldn't notice. After dinner Ron managed to retune the telly, and while we were watching a repeat of some British comedy or other, Fran started saying how much she'd enjoyed the day out, and how sorry she was to be leaving in two days' time. Then she turned to me and said, 'You've got another week to go, haven't you? I don't suppose you'd like to swap tickets with me, would you? This climate doesn't seem to agree with you, and I'm sure you'd be a lot happier back home in good old England.'

Well, I had to hand it to her. In spite of all I'd thought about her, I had to admit she was astute, and to be perfectly honest my heart leapt at the thought of getting back to my daily routine, and being in walking distance of my doctor and my local pharmacist. So that's what we did. Fran and I exchanged bookings, and here I am back at Ben Gurion airport. They've just announced that my flight has been delayed for another two hours but I don't mind. In a funny way it reminds me of home. It was lovely seeing Ron and Cynthia again, and in their new surroundings, but just between you and me I can't think why I agreed to go in the first place.

# WILLARD

*Sunday evening 25th September*

Having driven down from London, parked the car in a huge hangar on the Southampton docks, and lugged two cases (one of props) up the gangway of the cruise ship *The Prince Consort*, here I am, about to spend two glorious weeks exploring the Mediterranean. As entertainers, Willard and I will be considered members of the crew, and I found an official-looking letter in my cabin inviting me to meet the captain and his officers at a drinks party in his cabin at seven p.m. Knocked on Willard's door opposite to check if he'd got one. Without opening he answered, 'Yes but I'm not keen.' Wonder why? Perhaps he doesn't drink. Don't know him very well yet, although in the car he did tell me a bit about himself.

Married, but, I gathered, not happily. Apparently his wife doesn't appreciate his 'need for creative space', and is constantly badgering him to earn more by giving piano lessons. He said something like: there are those who 'do' and those who teach, and what he has to offer is personal and precious to him and can't be shared. He's a plump man, I would guess in his late thirties, not good-looking but there's something about him, a strange quality. He has a teenage daughter who is close to his wife and he feels excluded. Felt quite sorry for him. He had stood in for my accompanist Pete last month when I did my one-woman show in Milton Keynes, and picked it up really quickly, even the tricky bits. Said he loved the show, especially the mini musicals, so when Pete couldn't make it, I was really chuffed Willard agreed to literally accompany me on this trip. Mind you, getting a free cruise as well as being paid, in exchange for three forty-five-minute performances, isn't too bad a deal.

Off now for a quick shower, then off to meet the naval high-ups.

*Monday 26th September*

At last night's get together tried to be sociable and jolly, but after two glasses of champagne began to feel the rolling of the ship and had to beat a retreat. As I was leaving Willard appeared still wearing the clothes he'd driven down in and looking pretty scruffy. Thought I ought to say something but didn't feel up to it.

Spent a rough night. Some time during the early hours my phone rang. It was Willard who mumbled about sharing something or other and being together. I wasn't pleased and said so (can't remember what exactly) and slammed the phone down. Remembered the call when I woke up this morning and hope it isn't going to affect our working relationship. Also pray it doesn't mean I'm going to have to deal with any sort of advances from him. I suppose I'll have to make things clear if and when an opportunity arises. Damn, I really don't need this!

Still not feeling too good so decided to visit doctor for restorative injection. First show tomorrow night, so to Willard's cabin to suggest we do a run-through in the theatre before dinner. No answer. Pushed note under door. At lunch, no Willard. Spent afternoon recuperating in deckchair by pool. Still no sign of him. At teatime got anxious so set off to look for him. Found him in empty theatre playing some very cool jazz. He glanced up, then carried on playing. Wondered if he'd mention the phone call, or whether I should. The music for my show was on piano, unopened. After a few minutes:

Me: Sorry to interrupt, but how about us going through some stuff.

W: (*goes on playing*) Stuff?

Me: Well, I thought we might just run through any…

W: For me or for you?

Me: (*nervous laugh*) Well, both.

W. *stops playing.*

W: Has anything changed since I played the show in Milton Keynes?

Me: No. Well, yes. I mean that was the full show. This is only forty-five minutes, so…

W: Have you got a running order?

Me: (*getting a bit miffed*) Of course.

*I show him running order.*

W: (*peruses same*) Looks okay to me. Anything *you're* unsure of?

Me: (*floundering*) Maybe we could just check the tempo of… say, *Margie*?

W: Sure. That's my job.

*He scrabbles through music, finds copy of* Margie.

*He plays, I sing. The tempo is perfect.*

W: Okay?

Me: Yup, absolutely.

W: (*leaning towards me*) As long as you know what you're doing, we'll be fine.

The run-through was over. I have a sinking feeling that the phone call has provoked him into being 'awkward'.

At dinner the *maitre d'* seated us at a table set aside for the entertainers. There's Ron, a stand-up comedian who will be warm-up man for anyone who needs him (I declined his offer), a pianist called Ian (obviously gay), and Sabrina, his singing partner. They've been booked to entertain the passengers in the Starlight Bar every evening from nine to eleven. Last and probably least there are Marcia and Bill, a remarkably dull couple I would guess in their early forties, who do a telepathy act of some sort that involves playing cards. Having introduced ourselves we tried to include them in our conversation, but they barely spoke. From time to time Marcia would lean in to Bill and murmur something, and he would either nod, or briefly murmur something back.

The meal was over and coffee had just been served when Marcia leaned in once more to whisper something to Bill. Willard, sitting opposite her, said loudly, 'I'm sorry, I missed that. What did you say?' The poor woman simply stared at him.

'Hello!' he yodelled, 'I said sorry, I missed that, what did you say?' He repeated it as to an idiot, something with which I was to become all too familiar. Marcia opened her mouth, then closed it and looked to Bill for help.

'My wife,' said Bill, 'was talking to me.'

'Ah, now that's really interesting!' said W. Sensing trouble, the rest of us looked on with some unease. 'You surprise me. You see, I assumed that as you work telepathically, you two would have no use for speech when communicating with one another. So it follows that when you *do* speak out loud, as it were...'

I had no wish to hear any more so I made my excuses and fled. Headed for the Starlight and was joined by Ian and Sabrina. What was all that about at dinner? Don't ask me, I replied, he's only my accompanist. Large drinks all round, then they began their first set and I went to my cabin for a much needed early night.

*Tuesday 27th September*

Got up late, scribbled note to W. 'requesting' final run-through in theatre at five p.m., and pushed it under his door. Spent day on deck by pool, going through material for tonight's show, then down to theatre to sort out props. W. showed up at five p.m. sharp and we ran through the musical items. Only one problem arose when the manuscript just said 'transpose key' rather than it being written out. Still, I suppose he was entitled to complain.

W. arrived late for dinner wearing his dress suit ready for the show, and proceeded to knock back the contents of the bottle of wine he'd ordered, ignoring the rest of the table. Having thought he might be teetotal I was taken aback at the rate he was drinking and wondered if I ought to say something, but I was reluctant to raise the temperature and just prayed it wouldn't affect his performance. As it happened I needn't have worried; he played perfectly and, much to my relief, even seemed to enjoy it.

The show went well enough, though the theatre was only half full and the reception hard to judge. After our curtain calls, I waited backstage for the auditorium to clear so that I could pack away my bits and pieces. W. had disappeared. My pianists usually help me while we discuss how the show went, and I thought W. could at least have had the manners to say something, even if it was only goodbye! I hauled the case of props down to my cabin and went up to the Starlight. Ian and Sabrina were sitting on high stools at the bar with W., and in front of him was what I learned later to be his favourite tipple, a pint of Guinness and a couple of whiskey chasers. He lifted a lazy hand, a wide toothy grin across his podgy, complacent face.

'Hello, love!' Then he turned back to Ian and Sabrina, presumably to continue from where he'd left off. I sat down opposite them and ordered a glass of wine.

'How did the show go?' Sabrina called across the bar.

'Didn't Willard say?'

'No, he just said ask you.'

'Really? How do you think it went, Willard?' I asked.

'It's your show, you tell me.'

'It went fine, but I'd have appreciated a little help with clearing up.'

'Not my job, love.'

'Well how about a little civility instead of heading off without a word?' I was getting angry.

'Eh! Hold it!'

He got off the stool and moved around the bar towards me.

'Did I play good?' he asked with a nasty smile. 'Well, did I?'

'That's not the point.'

'Oh? What is the point then?'

He reached me, and putting his face close to mine, continued, ' I do what I do and you do what you do. My job is to play, not keep you company or give opinions. If you want opinions, go ask your effing audience!'

Short of flinging my drink at him I thought it wiser to knock it back and leave. Oh Lord, what have I let myself in for?

*Wednesday 28th September*
*Tangier – Morocco*

Today into the Port of Tangier. We'd been warned about the guides who swarm around the disembarking passengers trying to sell their services, or pick up fares to taxi you around the city. I thought it a good idea to have a guide, and as I followed W. ashore a young man in the group that surrounded us caught my eye. I was about to point him out when W. started talking gibberish at them.

Me: What on earth are you doing?
W: (*under his breath*) If they don't understand us they'll eff off!
Me: Well I think we should have a guide.
W: No.

He talked more gibberish, and the guides shrugged and left. He stopped to roll what was probably a joint, and pulling the smoke into his face strode past me towards a bustling market square. I followed, and found the young guide I had noticed hopping beside me.

'You take me, me good guide.'

I caught up with W. just as he was about to turn into a narrow cobbled lane.

W: I'm going down there… Coming?
Me: No. I think I'll go with this guide.
W: Fine.

And he strutted off, raising a hand without turning.

I was quite happy to pay the guide… possibly too much, but what the hell! First he took me to marvel at an eight-hundred-year-old banyan tree, then through a maze of narrow streets to a little tree-lined square with several cafés. I declined his suggestion to stop for a coffee, and on we went to the crowded Grand Succo Market. One stall selling brightly patterned footwear caught my eye, and I managed to barter a pair of embroidered slippers from fifteen down to eleven dollars, and some leather sandals from eleven down to seven! Hot and tired, I returned to the ship just in time for a late lunch on deck. Unwrapped my purchases, to find that although the slippers were there, the leather sandals had been replaced by an enormous pair of men's thongs! So much for my bargaining powers. The cabin steward was delighted with them.

Before dinner to Starlight for a cocktail. Ian and Sabrina provided some really classy entertainment while people chattered. What a thankless job! W. was sitting with a middle-aged couple at one of the side tables, holding forth. When the couple saw me they waved me over and introduced themselves: Laurence and Betty Goddard, a very Yorkshire couple. Said they'd seen the show last night and were very complimentary. Thought a lot of the humour had gone over the heads of the rather elderly audience. Offered me a drink, then asked W. if he would like another. He accepted in spite of the almost full pint in front of him.

First sitting with the same fellow diners. W. has the most embarrassing table manners. The first thing he does is tuck his napkin into his shirt collar as a bib; then he leans over his plate and shovels the food in. It is now his habit to order a bottle of wine for himself, and in the unlikely event that any is left, takes the remainder with him down to his cabin. Ron the comic is teetotal, and it seems Marcia and Bill don't drink either, so Ian, Sabrina and I decided to take turns in buying and sharing.

At one point during dinner W. whispered loudly: 'Do we have to sit here opposite this sodding awful couple for the rest of the cruise?' He really is something else. Still, we have to work together and we're more or less trapped on board, so I dare not fall out with him. I asked quietly if he would like me to ask the *maître d'* if he could change us to the second sitting. W. shrugged, pulled off his bib, grabbed his bottle and left. On my way out I did ask the *maître d'* but he said he'd have to consult. I turned on my most persuasive 'charm' and he weakened. He would try for tomorrow night. So that, for the moment, is that.

Tonight it was Marcia and Bill's turn to entertain the passengers in the main lounge. Saw W. on the other side and crept into a seat out of his line of vision. Joined by Laurence and Betty Goddard, the couple I'd met earlier. They asked about me and W. and I was quick to point out that ours was a purely working relationship. They visibly relaxed. Said they couldn't make him out and he was difficult to hold a conversation with. It was comforting to know I wasn't alone!

The show itself was dull and predictable, although the elderly audience seemed to enjoy it. Afterwards W. came over and sat in the seat beside me.

Me: How did you like the show?
W: More than I expected, and less than I anticipated. Very droll.

No idea what he meant. Awkward silence. Then W. said: 'Did you hear that two Guyanese members of the crew missed the ship today?'

Me: You mean they were left ashore?
W: (*slowly and deliberately*) THEY MISSED THE SHIP, SO WHERE ELSE WOULD THEY HAVE BEEN LEFT?

Sensing trouble, Laurence said quickly: 'Poor bastards! That'll mean instant dismissal.'

We sat again in silence, and it must have penetrated W.'s thick skin that no one was going to buy him a drink or engage him in conversation, so he pushed himself out of his chair and said he was going to try the Caribbean bar because he was bored with the Starlight, and was I coming with him. No, I'd rather stay put, so off he went.

The Goddards really are a delightful couple. Asked me if I had a partner back home. No, only a border collie called Crispin who was being looked after by a friend, and who I missed hugely. Laurence then confessed himself to be a self-made millionaire! Started out owning a small bakery in Hull, decided to make pork pies using his grandmother's recipe and has never looked back. Owns a chain of shops in the North, and is planning to 'infiltrate' the South. They told me they were on their honeymoon and had only been married for a fortnight, and, Betty said with a laugh, before she met him she'd accepted the fact that she would probably remain a spinster. Laurence's first wife had died a few years before, and he had two grown-up sons who had their own families and their own interests. These didn't include his bakery business, but did, he joked, include its profits.

He and Betty had met six months ago when Laurence had had a minor heart attack and been taken into hospital. She had been a health visitor at the time, and when Laurence was discharged she'd been dispatched to check on him daily. One day as she was driving away, she'd had an overwhelming urge to go back, and found him on the floor in the hallway. She said she'd tried to resuscitate him but he wasn't responding, and she knew she was too late.

'Then I grasped both his hands in mine, and with all the strength of my mind, I willed him to come back. I kept saying it, come back Laurence, come back, you must come back. And he did: suddenly his eyes flickered and opened.'

She couldn't go on and I confess I was moved too, but I wanted to know more. I noticed she hadn't said 'with all my strength of mind' which is what is usually said, but 'with all the strength of my mind'. It may sound ridiculous and it was a very slight point, but it made me wonder.

'That's amazing, Betty,' I said, 'you must have a very special gift! Do you think you're psychic?'

Before she could reply Laurence spoke up:

'Of course not, Sheila,' he said with a laugh, 'none of that mumbo jumbo! It was just one of those things, and I was jolly lucky she turned up when she did. Between you and me, even though she didn't know it at the time, she couldn't have lived without me, and I probably wouldn't have lived without her! And in the unlikely case that it might happen again, I decided the only way to make sure she stayed by me was to marry her.'

They laughed, and as he took her hand and kissed it the tenderness between them was palpable. A real tonic, especially after spending time with that impossible bastard, Willard.

They left soon after and I went down to my cabin, but I couldn't get them out of my mind, so I decided to take myself up to the Starlight for a nightcap. Much to my annoyance I found W. holding forth to a young couple who looked desperate, poor souls, so I left swiftly, and escaped to bed.

*Thursday 29th September*

Next show is on Friday, but as we'll be spending the day exploring Toulon, decided we ought to rehearse today. Am going to rearrange the running order and put in a different 'mini musical'. W. not answering his phone so left a note under his door saying rehearsal in the theatre at twelve p.m. Wonder if he'll turn up.

*Later*

This is getting ridiculous! W. did turn up but an hour late. He was in a foul mood, irritable about changes, saying things like, 'That won't make any difference,' and 'No good blaming the audience for your own inadequacies!' This from a man who said he loved the show when he saw it! As for the mini musicals, he actually said: 'I can't see why you're so keen on brevity!!' Good God, the whole point is to perform the entire musical in under three minutes! He accused me of being devoid of any musical sensitivity, and then banged out the opening bars of *My Fair Lady*, saying it sounded like *Three Blind Mice*! Rehearsing with him was like dragging a body through mud so eventually I suggested we call it a day. What I really want to do is throw him and the show overboard. Will have to keep a reasonable working relationship going, though God knows how.

Ended up having lunch together at the snack bar by the pool. We sat silent, he chomping and shovelling. Eventually I tried to smooth his ruffled ego by complimenting him on his playing. Discovered he'd only got to bed at six a.m. and hadn't found my note till twelve thirty. Arranged to rehearse again at five forty-five.

To my surprise he was already there improvising jazz, and I have to admit he's pretty damn good. He knows it, and clearly didn't want to break off and rehearse, so I just stood around getting more and more frustrated. Eventually I said: 'Okay, let's rehearse.' He played a long 'finish', then put *My Fair Lady* on the stand in front of him.

We get stuck on the opening phrase.

W: You're not consistent. You keep timing it differently.
Me: No I don't. You're coming in too early.

W: I don't know what you want.
Me: Just wait until I come in. Don't come in ahead of me.
W: (*shrugs*)

*Of course* he then comes in late.

Me: Look, just cross out the next two bars. Okay?

He makes a big deal of taking his pencil out of his breast pocket and crossing out the next two bars. We struggle through a few more songs but the atmosphere is icy.

I say, 'Let's take a break,' meaning: let's stop before the eggshells I'm treading on cut my feet to ribbons.

W. gives me a long look, then slowly shuts the music.

Me: (*only because I have to*) Oh, about dinner.
W: What about dinner?
Me: I think I've managed to change our first sitting to the second, so you won't have to sit with those people.
W: No need. I don't mind sitting with them.
Me: Look, you complained about spending the rest of the cruise with them and I went to a lot of trouble to change it.
W: I said I don't mind sitting with them.
Me: That's not what you… Just tell me what it is you want.
W: I can put up with anything if I have to, it doesn't bother me.
Me: Well it bothers me. What exactly do you want?
W: (*once more as to a dimwit*) I am quite happy sitting opposite that man and his pathetic wife for the entire cruise. Okay? Got it? So that's fine.
Me: No, it's not fine. It is absolutely, bloody well NOT FINE!

I storm off. No intention of giving him the satisfaction of seeing me cry.

*Later*

Having showered away some of my fury, I decided that what matters is the show. We have to work tomorrow night, so I'll write him a note saying I would be going to the second sitting, and then to the film (*Mrs Doubtfire*) and he'd be welcome to join me.

Before dinner had drink in Starlight. No sign of W., nor at second sitting where I found myself entirely alone feeling spare and angry. No sign of W. at the film nor later in Starlight. On way back to cabin checked the Caribbean. Not there either. And so to bed.

*Friday 30th September*
*Toulon – France*

Met W. on deck at breakfast which is self-service. The amount on his plate always astonishes me. Seemed in a good mood, and when I bravely suggested a quick run-through before we went ashore, was quite amenable. Then, of course, the trouble began. During these rehearsals he doesn't talk, he lectures, but we did manage to iron out a few glitches. Then, silly me, I suggested we go on shore together. Will I never learn!

It was raining… or rather, there was a very slight drizzle. As we left the Marina, W. decided he had to buy an umbrella and became obsessed with the idea. He darted off peering into any likely shop, leaving me trailing behind. His blood was up, he was on the hunt for an umbrella and he wasn't going to give up until he found one. We happened upon a huge shopping mall, which I later discovered is the biggest shopping mall on the Var (whatever that is).

W. stops and points triumphantly at a sign that reads C&A. The British are here! This must, by definition, mean that here umbrellas will be found, and in he marches, me following. We ride up and down escalators, W. frantic for the elusive gamp. The man is wild-eyed, possessed, and I trot after him getting more and more hacked off. For God's sake, I didn't come to

Toulon to explore a shopping mall! I grab his arm and tell him I will wait outside in the square. The sky is clear and sunny, and I sit myself on one of the wooden benches. And lo! Here he comes, flushed with success and clutching not one, but *two* umbrellas! He hands one to me. No thanks, not for me, and instantly I regret saying it. I tell him sorry, I shouldn't have said that, to which he replies I'm effing sorry too, and I hope it effing well pours! And with that he tucks both umbrellas under his arm and lopes off. I wander around the streets of the old town, buy myself a croissant and coffee off a stall somewhere, and go back on board. I'm not in the mood for sightseeing.

I decided my refusal of the umbrella was on a par with his refusal of the second sitting… we'd both gone to some trouble and both been rejected. Wrote what I hoped was a jokey apology and pushed it under his door. Later he phoned and we had a surprisingly pleasant conversation. Thought at last we were getting somewhere.

Our port of call tomorrow is Livorno, and he told me he'd booked himself onto a coach trip from Livorno to Florence, and if I wanted to go I'd better hurry up and book. He knew I was planning to go and he could have booked for both of us. Anyway, went up and booked on the same coach. Will probably regret it.

Rehearsed at six and surprise surprise, we're back to uneasy relationship. First he criticised my use of the microphone, then insisted on having the piano angled away from me which means we'll have no eye contact. Final straw: he doesn't want to take any curtain calls, will just walk off stage and leave me to it. Well, he can do what he wants. Great rapport there'll be between us on stage tonight!

Before the show we were both at the first sitting. *Maître d'* raised an eyebrow and I shrugged and nodded in W.'s direction. The Goddards sent me over a really good bottle of wine, and although I don't usually drink before a show, I had a glass with Ian and Sabrina. When I offered it to W. he declined. I asked why, and he said he was trying out various wines in turn, and he didn't want to be sidelined!

The man is unhinged.

*Later*

Show went well in spite of unpleasantness at rehearsal. As anticipated, I was left alone on stage for the curtain calls. W. disappeared as he'd done last time, and when I went up to Starlight, found him sitting at the bar with an elderly man who had the glazed look usually seen on his victims. I sat at one of the side tables listening to Ian and Sabrina. He's a better pianist than she a singer, but they work really well together. Bought them a drink, then asked the barman to send one over to W. and left before it reached him.

*Saturday 1st October*
*Livorno – Italy*

Briefly crossed paths with W. at breakfast. He was a bit too hearty, called me 'Sheila', not 'love' as he usually does. Why should that bother me? I must stop… he's really getting to me. On coach felt I ought to keep the seat next to me for him, God knows why, so when I saw him I hopped off and waved. During the drive he read, then slept and snored. When he did surface I asked what his plans were for the day. Mumbled something about taking stock. Told him I wanted to spend time looking at Michelangelo's David, and we started quite a reasonable conversation on the subject of sculpture. A long lecture followed with him saying the medium shouldn't influence one's judgement, and I said how can it not? He was off, and by the time we arrived in Florence my ears were ringing and steam was coming out of his. It was clear we were going to go our separate ways.

Straight to the Gallerie dell'Academia and the David. Spent an hour or so just looking at it from every angle, then sat against a wall and looked some more. Eventually dragged myself away and headed for the Duomo. Climbed Giotto's

Campanile and the view of the city was incredible. I had promised my friend Hesta that, if I could, I'd buy her a suede jacket in Florence. She'd been here with her then lover and he'd refused to let her buy one, but that's another story. I found her a really nice reasonably priced jacket in a leather shop just off one of the market squares, then had a plate of pasta and a glass of wine at a trattoria. On to look at the Ponte Vecchio, then back to the coach station, buying myself a cheap leather handbag on the way.

W. was already inside the coach, looking at a map of the city and smelling heavily of garlic. Greeted me curtly, and when I asked what he'd done, replied: 'Just wandered around. I'm no queue joiner.' I asked if he'd bought any presents. 'Who for?'

'Well, your wife maybe? Or your daughter?'

'I don't buy affection.'

Oh please!!

Back on board we were too late for the first sitting, so agreed we'd go in to the second, but later when I went down there was no sign of him. About to dine alone when Betty Goddard came over and invited me to join them at their table. Half way through meal looked over and saw W. at our table on his own, eyes down, elbows akimbo, shovelling and chomping. Felt a bit guilty but after all he had been late, so as I left I went over and explained. Without looking up he said: 'I like my own company.' Well, I suppose somebody has to.

To pop concert on deck with the Goddards. No sign of W. Then to bed.

### Sunday 2nd October
### Monte Carlo

We slid into Monte Carlo at eight a.m. Went ashore on my own. Walked through parks in the Casino grounds, had lunch in a small local café, then climbed up to the Jardin Exotique. When I got back found a note from Laurence and Betty G.

inviting me to have lunch with them tomorrow on shore in Ajaccio, our next stop.

Over dinner discovered the trick of how to engage W. in conversation. He only responds when you ask about himself and his opinions, and it's essential to look intrigued by what he says. It was working well, until half way through the meal he turned his attention to the couple he had been so nasty about. Pretending to be interested in them he teased them cruelly, and it was embarrassing and upsetting to watch them rise to the bait. The only thing I could think of to get his attention was to offer to pay for the bottle of wine he had just ordered, which he accepted casually as though it was his due. At the end of the meal he ordered himself a large port, then raised it in my direction and, needless to say, swallowed it down in one.

*Later*

There was a classical music recital given by the small orchestra who entertain the passengers in the main lounge most afternoons. I sat at the back, while W. placed himself in the front row, bravo-ing and applauding at every opportunity. When it was over I went up to the Starlight, and soon W. arrived and joined me. Having bought himself a drink he proceeded to shred the orchestra's performance to pieces. I'd had enough, but as I was leaving Ian and Sabrina, who had just finished their set, called me over.

Ian: Hope you don't mind. We really didn't want to sit with Willard.
Sabrina: What's his problem? Honestly, he doesn't half go on. Once he starts you can't get a word in edgeways!
Me: Tell me about it!
Ian: How do you work with him?
Me: With great difficulty.

Feel comforted to know I have allies. Looked across and saw W. had joined a couple at one of the tables. The barman was delivering a pint of Guinness and a whiskey chaser, and I watched as the man signed the bill.

*Monday 3rd October*
*Ajaccio – Corsica*

This morning told W. I'd planned to lunch ashore with Goddards. Ridiculous, but once again I felt guilty about him. Still, if he had joined us, the drinks bill would have soared.

We lunched in a restaurant called McGregor's, cuisine a cross between Italian and French. The view of the harbour was splendid, and the food… after an interminable wait… delicious. Two excellent bottles of local wine, and, although we planned to visit the Napoleon Museum after lunch, hot and a little drunk we decided to go back to ship for a siesta.

This evening knocked on W.'s door and found him sitting on his bed reading. Asked if he was coming to the curry dinner on deck tonight. No, he's going to get an early night. Tells me he's on water and indicates litre bottle on bedside table. Next to it, two bananas and an orange. I'll give it less than a day. After dining alfresco, to main lounge for jazz night. Thought W. would show up for it, but no sign.

*Tuesday 4th October*
*Port Mahon – Menorca*

Last stop before returning to Southampton. Lovely day on my own just strolling around. Late lunch in café near marina to drool over millionaires' yachts, then back on board for late-afternoon swim and sunbathe. Found W. at the first sitting with a large plateful in front of him and a bottle of red at his elbow.

This evening all the entertainers were invited to the captain's cabin for drinks at nine. Party was very crowded so didn't stay long and went to lounge where the pianist from the orchestra was tinkling away. Ron the comic turned up, and I bought him an alcohol-free lager. We bitched enjoyably about Willard. Bed at eleven thirty.

*Wednesday 5th October*

Three days left before we reach Southampton.

At breakfast discovered most people including W. were hung over. Apparently last night's party had lasted through the night. Spent morning in last of the sun before we sail into murky weather. Stood on deck as we sailed through the Straits of Gibraltar where the Mediterranean joins the Atlantic. Hard to believe you can see Spain on one side and Morocco on the other. Afternoon more sun and tried to write a lyric that's been simmering in my head about male chauvinists.

W. and I should have rehearsed for the last show tomorrow night, but I dread, not only asking him, but working with him. Decided to give myself a break and leave it till tomorrow. First sitting, no sign of W. Relieved but slightly uneasy. No sign of him in Starlight bar or lounge. Phoned his cabin. No reply. Thought I'd try the Caribbean, and there he was, sitting at the bar on his own. Everyone, it seems, now tries to avoid him. Poor sod.

*Thursday 6th October*

At breakfast W. and I sat at different tables, both making a feature of pretending to read. It must be clear to everyone that we loathe each other. It took some courage to go over and ask him if we could rehearse while the theatre was free. He wasn't keen but said okay. During the half-hour rehearsal he was cutting and nasty. Banged out the introductions, then gave me a long lecture on 'musical grammar'. Final straw when he refused to repeat a phrase at the end of a song.

W: Why repeat it?
Me: Because that's where the laugh is.
W: It's musically inept!
Me: I don't care! Just repeat it, okay?

W: I will do whatever you like, but it's wrong.
Me: Willard, it's not opera, it's not recitative… it's a tagline!
W: Then it doesn't matter WHAT I bloody play, does it?

*Later*

Show went quite well, but vibes between W. and I make it hard work. Also poor attendance. As I was packing props after show, to my surprise W. put his head round the curtain and said, 'See you for a drink in the Caribbean.' Decided it might be an opportunity to make peace. He had a glass of wine waiting for me (first drink he's bought me!). Ian was with him and told me he'd seen the show. Was very complimentary. I bought a round, then Ian bought one, then ignoring us W. ordered himself yet another pint plus chaser. He certainly can hold his liquor! He began making innuendos about Ian's sexuality, suggesting it might do him good to have sex with a woman. 'Everyone should try everything at least once!' he said. Then, 'I'm sure Sheila will oblige.' Ian and I were both thoroughly embarrassed, and I was livid. I got up to leave, but as I reached for my cabin keys which were on the table, W. grabbed them.

W: (*getting up*) Come on, Ian, let's all go down to her cabin.
Ian: Don't be silly, Willard. Give her back her keys.
W: Come on, she'll follow us. You're going to love this!

And he left the bar jiggling the keys in the air. Ian followed W. out, saying, 'Hang on, I'll sort this out.' I sat there for what seemed an age, and eventually Ian returned holding the keys. No sign of W.

Me: How did you manage it?
Ian: I told him it was a great idea, I really fancied you, but I'd prefer to do it without his help.

It was three in the morning, I was tired, I was miserable, and I went to bed. Alone.

*Friday 7th October*

Southampton early tomorrow, so today started to pack. Had lunch with Laurence and Betty and we exchanged addresses and phone numbers. They invited me to stay with them in their country pile for a weekend sometime. Just might do that.

At dinner W. and I made a point of ignoring each other. Truth to tell I've no idea how to deal with the situation. Quick visit to Starlight to say goodbye to Ian and Sabrina, then to cabin to finish packing. Saw W.'s door was ajar. Thought I ought to make an effort to break the ice, after all there's the car journey home to get through, so I put my head in.

Me: Have you been to the crew office yet to sort out your papers?
W: No. I've still got to find exactly where it is.
Me: Well, you go up to the…
W: It's all right, I'll find it.
Me: It's on the first…
W: (*as to an idiot*) IT'S ALL RIGHT, I'LL FIND IT.

I leave and slam my own cabin door.

*Saturday 8th October*

What can I say about the drive back to London?

The day was dull and overcast, as was the atmosphere in the car. Unbelievably, not a single word was spoken throughout the two hours' journey until we reached the outskirts of London, driving past Sunbury. I asked whether he knew the directions to his house from where we were.

W: I know.
Me: Well, can you tell me, because I like to know ahead of time
    where I'm going.
W: I'll tell you.

I drive some more. We reach Twickenham.

Me: Where now?
W: I'll tell you.

I bite my tongue and drive on. We get to Richmond and I
know we must turn off at some point to get to Wandsworth,
where he lives.

Me: Shouldn't we be…
W: Here! At this roundabout! Turn right!

It's a last-minute instruction. I swerve and go right, fuming.
We sit in mutual loathing. From time to time he snaps out
short commands, I tighten my grip on the steering wheel and
do as I'm told, and finally, finally and at last, I'm told to pull
over and stop.

Willard opens the car door, heaves himself out slamming
the door shut. He lopes around the car, opens the boot,
removes his case and shuts the lid hard so that the car
shudders. And then without a word, he strides away. I quickly
press the button that automatically opens the passenger
window.

'Hey, Willard!'

He stops, puts down the case, turns, and takes slow,
deliberate steps back to the car.

'Sorry to bother you,' I say, 'but how do I get back to
civilisation?'

Willard leans his head in through the open window, his
face only inches from mine. His round, protruding blue eyes

are icy, his fat lips zipped into a mean, nasty smile. Then he speaks slowly, deliberately.

'You're *in* effing civilisation,' he snarls.

So I hit the button, sending the window whizzing upwards, and as I accelerate away his yowling tells me that he's still in the land of the living.

Ah well, better luck next time.

# THE GODDARDS

I'd been back from the cruise with Willard for about a month, when I received a letter from the Goddards saying how much they'd enjoyed meeting me, and expressing the hope that I'd come and visit them in their country house on the outskirts of Hull. Knowing how devoted I was to my dog Crispin, they suggested I bring him with me, which made their offer more appealing, since I wouldn't have to organise a dog-sitter.

I was involved in recording a television series at the time so I wrote back thanking them, and asked if we could put a rain check on their offer. Time passed, Christmas came, and I sent a card with a promise to visit in the New Year. As expected a reciprocal card arrived signed with both their names, but written, which I thought a little odd, in the same hand. Odder still, on the back of the envelope was scrawled: *Please come soon as. B.* There was something about it that decided me to pay the promised visit sooner rather than later, and I phoned to arrange a mutually convenient weekend.

'Eh, chuck, lovely to hear your voice!' Laurence boomed. 'What can I do you for? When are you coming up to see us, eh?'

'Well, I got your card and thought if I left it any longer you'd forget me altogether!'

'Forget you, lass! Never!' He laughed. 'I still tell folk up here about meeting you on that cruise and they're right impressed. Don't rub shoulders with many celebrities up here in the North you know. So, when can you come?'

'How about the fourteenth? It'll have to be a short weekend, I'm afraid, because of rehearsals. I could drive up early on the Saturday morning and leave on Sunday after lunch.'

'Not long enough, but that sounds just fine.'

'Oh, and by the way, did you mean it when you included Crispin in your invitation?' I asked.

'Of course! Matter of fact Betty's just acquired a young dog herself. Got it from a friend who for some reason couldn't cope. Bit of a pest, bit too full of beans, so hopefully Crispin will teach him some manners.'

It was a long drive, and once we left the main road and ventured into the countryside I was grateful for the detailed directions Laurence had sent. The roads became uncomfortably narrow, banking here and there to allow oncoming traffic to pass, and it was mid afternoon by the time we arrived at our destination. The house stood at the end of a potholed road behind a low brick wall with wrought-iron security gates that stood proud of it by a good half metre. Resisting the temptation to step over the boundary wall, I pressed the button on the security box.

'Sheila, you're here! Come in!'

A buzzer sounded, the gates opened, and I drove down the short gravel path and parked next to a mud-spattered four-by-four standing near a row of trimmed hedges. Crispin leapt out and headed for the nearest tree just as Laurence appeared at the front door. He strode towards me, greeted me with a warm embrace and, retrieving my bags from the back seat, put an arm around my shoulders and walked me back to the house. As he opened the door, Crispin dived past our legs and scampered down the hallway, and, calling him, I hurried in after him. He stopped at a closed door and began whimpering and scratching.

'He's not silly your dog, is he, eh?' Laurence said with a laugh. 'He can tell it's the kitchen, and Betty's in there with that mutt of hers. I won't let her have it in the rest of the house. I don't really want it in there either but Betty raised the roof, so I said it can stay in there as long as she's in there with him.' He tapped sharply on the door. 'Open up, Betty,' he called, 'Sheila's here with her dog. And make sure that animal of yours stays inside!'

The door edged open and Crispin gave a nudge that swung it wide. He ran in, panting with excitement at the discovery of the pup, and the startled little dog scrambled past us into the hallway, squealing as it went. Crispin followed as did Betty, who made an ineffectual grab for the pup while I tried to grab Crispin's collar. At last she cornered the pup and was about to pick it up, when Laurence yanked it off its feet, and holding it at arm's length carried it back down the passage and dumped it onto the kitchen floor. Hurrying after him Betty scooped it up, cradling it in her arms, while I followed, holding Crispin by his collar. Laurence closed the door firmly. I was taken aback by Laurence's rough treatment of the pup, and decided if the chance arose later I would bring the subject up.

'I'm so sorry, Sheila! What a way to greet you!' said Betty apologetically, but I could tell the incident had upset her.

'Don't be silly,' I replied, 'you couldn't have arranged a more spectacular reception. It's so good to see you!' and crossing to her I kissed her cheek. 'What an adorable little dog! He's a Labrador, isn't he?'

'Yes, he is.' Betty nuzzled the little dog who seemed none the worse for his experience.

'What have you called him?'

'Toby,' she said, 'short, of course, for Thobias.'

'Of course,' I said with a laugh. 'Goes without saying.'

'Thobias! I ask you!' Laurence interjected. 'It's only a bloody dog, for God's sake! Look, never mind the dog, Betty, Sheila must be starving!' He turned to me. 'What would you like, lass? I daresay Betty can put something together for you, eh Betty?'

'Of course.'

Betty put the pup down on a rug in the corner of the room, and as she straightened up I noticed she was thinner than I remembered and her face looked a little drawn.

'I'm really not hungry,' I said, 'just a cup of tea would be fine.'

'Are you sure?' she asked.

'Betty, she said she's not hungry!' The irritation in his voice was unmistakable. 'We'll have tea in the sitting room. Just put a few biscuits on a plate, that'll do.'

As he opened the kitchen door and ushered me out with Crispin at my heels, he added, 'And since you've been messing about with that dog of yours, wash your hands before you start.'

I followed him down the passage wondering what I might have let myself in for.


Perhaps because Laurence had boasted he was a self-made millionaire I had expected the Goddards' house to be some sort of mansion, and although it was certainly large, it was squarely built in a modern style. Everything in the lounge we sat in was of good quality, but showed little good taste. Framed prints crowded the walls, glass and china baubles crammed the shelves, and various styles of furniture stood awkwardly side by side. Lamps with elaborate shades graced almost every available space, while the heavy hangings and patterned rugs vied with each other.

Laurence and I were chatting about the cruise (and, of course, Willard), when Betty came in wheeling a tea trolley set for two.

'Aren't you having tea with us?' I asked in surprise.

Before she could answer, Laurence interrupted.

'Betty's too busy cooking something special for you for tonight, but you'll catch up with her later. Right Betty?'

Again I thought I detected a slight edge in his voice, but as she left she gave me a cheerful smile and I dismissed the notion.

All the while Crispin had been curled up at my feet. Earlier as he had followed us out of the kitchen I had hesitated.

'What about Crispin?'

'It's all right, he can come,' Laurence had said as we headed down the passage. 'It's the yapping and the chewing that I can't be doing with.'

Nonetheless I couldn't help wondering if he was simply tolerating having my dog indoors in order to humour me. It was only when he showed me to my room and actually encouraged Crispin to follow us upstairs, that I decided I was being needlessly apprehensive. As Laurence opened the bedroom door Crispin had run in and leapt onto the large double bed, turning a circle or two and then settling down comfortably on the crisp, clean duvet. Hastily shooing him off, I avoided looking directly at my host in case he should be registering disapproval of this latest infringement of his house rules.

'You get yourselves sorted,' he said, seeming unfazed, 'and if you need owt give me a shout. We'll be having dinner at seven thirty. Our help, Mrs Coates, will be here any minute. She comes in of a morning to do the cleaning, and when we have guests like your good self she does the serving and washing up.'

'That lets me off the hook!' I joked, adding, 'Talking of dinner, do you mind if I give Crispin his food in the kitchen before we have our meal?'

'You do whatever suits you, lass,' he said, 'and it's drinks in the lounge at seven.'

'Fine. Will Betty be joining us?' I asked a little cautiously.

'Oh yes,' Laurence replied, 'she'll be there… as long as she can tear herself away from that bloody little pest of hers.'

As I unpacked my overnight bag I had mixed feelings. On the one hand it was good to see them again and I was pleased

Laurence had accepted Crispin as a more-or-less welcome guest, but I was thoroughly confused by his behaviour towards Betty, as well as his harsh attitude towards her dog. It seemed out of character for the humorous, kindly Laurence I'd spent time with on the cruise, and I decided when I could to talk to Betty on her own.

Having showered and changed, I took Crispin down to the kitchen to feed him. There was no sign of the pup or of Betty, but a rather sullen woman whom I took to be Mrs Coates was standing at the kitchen sink. She looked up, nodded briefly in my direction and resumed scrubbing at a saucepan. When Crispin had licked his bowl clean I opened the back door and followed him out. It was dark and more than a little chilly, and I wished I had brought my jacket with me. It wasn't long before the cold began to penetrate, and deciding Crispin had had enough time to do whatever it was he had to do, I called him. He didn't respond; instead I heard a muffled yapping coming from somewhere a little distance away. My eyes were getting accustomed to the gloom, and as I walked in the direction of the sound, I saw Crispin, head down, sniffing at the door of a shed. I tried the slatted wooden door but it held fast, and the yapping increased. I couldn't believe Laurence would actually have locked a puppy out here at night, and in this weather! I stood considering what to do. Betty was in no position to intervene, or the poor thing wouldn't have been there in the first place. It took an almost physical effort to stop myself heading back inside and confronting him, but I knew if I was to get anywhere I would have to be diplomatic and choose my moment; at least for the moment the pup was out of the weather. I called Crispin and, somewhat reluctantly, he followed me back into the warmth of the kitchen.

'Mrs Coates... It is Mrs Coates, isn't it?'

'Aye,' she said without turning her head.

'Mrs Coates, I'll be leaving Crispin... my dog... I'll be leaving him here in the kitchen while we have dinner. But you don't have to worry about him, he won't bother you.'

'Oh aye.'

I had brought Crispin's rug down with me, and laid it on the floor next to the pup's blanket.

'Mr Goddard said that would be fine. You don't mind, do you?'

'Aye,' came the enigmatic reply.

I had hoped that getting together for drinks before dinner would ease the situation, but I couldn't have been more wrong. Having handed me a vodka and tonic, Laurence placed himself with his back to the hissing gas fire with its fake logs, nursing a large whiskey and soda. He stood with his legs planted sturdily apart, as though defying a strong wind. Betty occupied the armchair opposite mine. She perched on the edge as though she was about to take flight, and held the dry sherry Laurence had given her without drinking. It was the first time I had had a chance to observe them as a couple since our encounters on board ship, and the contrast was marked. Now, in spite of my attempts to draw Betty out, she remained monosyllabic, while Laurence took every opportunity to dominate the conversation. When at last Mrs Coates appeared at the open door the feeling of relief was palpable.

'You don't want to leave it much longer,' she said gracelessly, 'it'll spoil.'

'Right, let's get on with it, then.'

Laurence drained his glass and, as Mrs Coates disappeared, motioned us to follow him into the ornately decorated dining room. At the far end a large painting, over-lacquered to the point of obscurity, loomed above a heavy mahogany sideboard on which stood several plates of various sizes and two promising looking bottles of wine. Three places had been laid at one end, and having fetched one of the bottles Laurence sat himself at the head of the table with Betty and me on either side. I had been hoping for an opportunity to bring the conversation around to the pup in the shed, but it was becoming clear this was not the time to broach that particular subject.

Mrs Coates had donned an overall for the occasion, serving each of the three courses with an air of morose indifference. Betty's cooking exceeded expectation and, after I had complimented her, even Laurence managed grudging approval. Once a glass or two had been drunk, the uneasy mood began to lift, and soon Betty and I were reminiscing about our fellow passengers on board ship. From time to time Laurence would interject with some detrimental remark directed at Betty; and, although at first she tried to ignore his jibes, it wasn't long before she lapsed into silence. I have often been in the company of couples who, for whatever reason, banter or argue in front of friends, but what I was witnessing was a display of malevolence, and by the time Mrs Coates had cleared away the dessert dishes Laurence's interjections were lacerating. My lame attempts to cajole Laurence into a kinder frame of mind were scoffed away. Instead he offered a refill from the almost-empty second bottle, and, when I declined, tipped the remainder into his own glass.

Mrs Coates appeared to announce she was off home and would deal with the washing-up in the morning, whereupon Betty rose, and with a hurried apology followed her out. I hoped she may have left to rescue the dog and bring it indoors, and I was about to raise the subject when Laurence leaned across the table and, grasping my hand, asked: 'Have you noticed how different Betty is? How much she's changed?'

Caught completely off guard, I nodded. If anyone had changed it was Laurence himself! Apart from anything else, I remembered him as a moderate drinker. Now here he was, much the worse for liquor. He released my hand and sank back into his chair.

'Sheila, when I married her, I had no idea she was... that she had ... *mental issues.*' He gave a short, bitter laugh. 'Mental bloody issues! I mean, you'd never have bloody suspected it, would you?'

Betty with mental issues? It seemed most unlikely. She'd seemed thoroughly normal on board ship, and indeed, on the few occasions I had been with her since I'd arrived, she had appeared much the same, if somewhat subdued.

'You know, of course, when I met her she was a health visitor… well, my health visitor after my heart attack. Do you remember her telling you how she'd found me lying in my hallway and she claimed she'd brought me back to life? And if it wasn't for her I'd be dead?'

How could I forget? It was still vivid in my mind. She'd said he'd had a fatal heart attack and she'd used her psychic powers to will him back to life.

'Well, let me tell you something, Sheila,' he continued. 'It didn't happen that way. She says I had a second heart attack… a fatal heart attack, and she brought me back to life. And at the time I believed her!' He laughed humourlessly. 'But here's the thing, Sheila. It's all in her mind. There was no fatal heart attack. I slipped on the polished floor, hit my head and lost consciousness, simple as that. I'd have come round whether she'd been there with her mumbo jumbo or not.'

'But Laurence,' I protested, coming to Betty's defence, 'she was a qualified health visitor! Surely she would have known the difference between…'

'Exactly! She knew all right!' he said triumphantly. 'And she wants me to believe she has the power to keep me alive. She wants me to be completely dependent on her.'

'Oh Laurence, how can you believe that!' I was shocked. 'Surely your doctor would have known what happened to you. What did he say?'

'Never saw him,' he said. 'Betty persuaded me I didn't need a doctor any more. Told me she could take care of me using her gifts, and I was so bloody grateful I agreed!'

'Then what made you change your mind?' I asked.

'I'll tell you, Sheila,' he said, warming to his theme. 'At first Betty fussed a bit about my health, insisting on… treating me or whatever they call it, but to be honest I thought it all a bit ridiculous. Still, I did my best to make things easy for her. I took over her money problems, I replaced her old car with a four-by-four we could both use, I even got Mrs Coates in to do the household chores. But Betty was becoming restless. Said she wanted to go back to work. I thought she meant as a health visitor, but it turned out she wanted to use her "gifts"… her "powers"! Well I tell you, Sheila, I wasn't having her set up shop in the house. And I wasn't having my phone jammed with calls from loonies!'

Clearly agitated, Laurence reached for his glass and drained it.

'Apart from anything else, if word got out that she was some sort of healer, it would be me who'd have to ferry her around. For some reason she refuses to drive the four-by-four, and I've no intention of playing chauffeur. Anyway, since I nipped that in the bud she's been getting more and more remote. She reads all the bloody time, gets books from the library, psychic stuff. It's not special gifts she has – she's using the power of suggestion to make me dependent on her!'

He sat back, watching for my response.

'But why on earth should she want you to be dependent on her?' I asked.

'Money!' he said. 'Money does funny things to people. Take my sons. Not interested in going into business with me, but they're always ready for a bloody handout, and not shy of asking. Well, they're out of my will. And now Betty wants control over me so she can get her hands on my money before I kick the bucket. Listen!' He stopped me before I could speak. 'Here's the thing. I think Betty's been playing cat and mouse with me, so now I'm returning the compliment. When I'm dead and gone she can have all I've got and welcome to it. But not while I'm here, alive and kicking. She's not going to get the better of me, and once she realises that, things will get back to being the way they should be.'

Laurence seemed to have sobered up and looked suddenly old and tired. He pushed back his chair and rose wearily.

'It's been a long day,' he said heavily, 'and I daresay we're both ready for bed.'

I lay awake in the dark in a state of confusion. On the one hand I felt some sympathy for Laurence finding himself in a dilemma of his own creating, but on the other hand I wondered whether he had reason to believe Betty had mental issues, as he put it. Nonetheless, his behaviour towards Betty was unacceptable, as was his treatment of the pup. Its whining had now resumed, and with Crispin curled up beside me I felt guilty and upset. The heating in the room was oppressive, and lying under the duvet made me sweat; sleep was out of the question. After a while the pup's whimpering had stopped, and I hoped the poor thing had exhausted itself to sleep. Throwing the duvet aside I snuggled up to my canine consoler, and tried not to think of what the morning might bring.

At breakfast Laurence showed no signs, either of our previous night's conversation or of his overindulgence. He chatted about this and that, taking little notice of Betty, who plainly had had little sleep. I waited for an opportune moment, and suggested she and I take the dogs out for a morning walk.

'You don't want to do that!' said Laurence. 'I think the three of us... sorry, four, including Crispin... should take a stroll down to the local later on for an early lunch before you head off home.'

'A pub lunch sounds an excellent idea,' I replied, 'but right now I need to blow away the cobwebs, and Crispin expects his regular constitutional. Come on, Betty, put on your walking shoes and let's get going.'

We strolled down the muddy lane in silence, passing a field where a couple of horses grazed, then at the far end turned into a wood. The sky was grey, the wind cold and sharp. Crispin ran free, revelling in new discoveries, whilst young Toby weaved and panted, pulling at Betty's lead. Suddenly she stopped, and turning to me said: 'As you can see, Sheila, things aren't working out between me and Laurence.'

'Yes, I noticed,' I said guardedly.

'I've probably made things worse by taking Toby on, but he's such a dear little thing, I couldn't resist.'

'How on earth did you get him to agree to let you have Toby in the first place?' I asked.

'God knows how his mind works. Perhaps I happened to ask him on a day when he was feeling a little generous-minded. Or maybe it was simply so that he could be nasty to the dog in order to get at me. He insists on keeping Toby in the shed at night, even in this weather. As a matter of fact I often spend my nights in the car with the dog.'

'You do *what*?' I asked, not sure I had heard her correctly. What she told me I found distressing.

The previous night Betty had waited until Laurence had gone to his room, then, as she had done before, she'd tiptoed down the stairs, taken the key of the shed off its hook by the kitchen door, retrieved the dog and, wrapping them both in her coat and his inadequate blanket, spent the night in the four-by-four. She was woken in the early morning, as she had been before, by Mrs Coates tapping on the car window. Displaying her usual stoic lack of curiosity, Mrs Coates had disappeared into the house and Betty followed, leaving the dog in the kitchen under Mrs Coates's indifferent eye while she soaked the chill out of her bones in a hot bath.

'And it wouldn't surprise me if Laurence knew,' she concluded.

'But that's ridiculous, Betty!' I said. 'This can't go on, you must talk to him.'

'He refuses to talk, Sheila, you've seen what he's become. Laurence is doing his best to undermine me and I'm helpless. There's nothing I can do about it.'

I wondered for an instant if Laurence had reason to doubt Betty's state of mind and she was perhaps paranoid.

'Do you remember how I saved Laurence's life when he had his fatal attack?'

'Of course I do,' I replied, noting her use of the word 'fatal'.

'Well, at first he was overwhelmingly grateful,' she said. 'He decided to stop seeing his doctor for checkups in spite of my trying to dissuade him. He kept saying that having me with my healing powers was all the medical attention he needed. Then one evening he had a couple of his cronies around for dinner. He'd had a fair amount to drink, and he began teasing me, telling them I believed I had psychic gifts and I could make things happen. I was embarrassed and upset, but I blamed the drink and tried to put it out of my mind. And then he started teasing me about it when we were on our own, and his remarks were getting more and more cutting and hurtful. Now he takes every opportunity to verbally abuse me. Well, you heard him yourself.'

She was finding it hard to speak, but after a moment she continued:

'If it was physical, if he hit me, at least I'd have something to show to prove it. But Sheila, the man is trying to make me doubt my sanity!'

'But why, Betty? Why on earth would he be doing it?'

'I have no idea. Perhaps he thinks I'm after his money. He thinks his sons are, and he's determined they won't get their hands on any of it. Maybe he's decided that I married him for his fortune. Nothing could be further from the truth!'

We walked on. I had no idea what to say to her, and was grateful when at last she spoke.

'I don't know whether you believe in such things, Sheila, but I know I have healing hands. When I was a health visitor I often used my hands as therapy when other treatments failed, and I do know I saved Laurence's life. It doesn't matter whether he believes it or not. *I* know. But... and I know this may sound ridiculous... I wonder whether he actually does believe I have some sort of psychic power, and it unnerves him. Perhaps that's why he's behaving like this. Did you know that because I'm no good at finance, Laurence said he'd take care of all our financial affairs and I signed everything over to him? I hadn't realised it meant I would have to ask him for money whenever I needed it. And when I do he grills me on how I plan to spend it, often whittling down the amount, or refusing me altogether.'

'I can't believe it! How humiliating!'

'You don't know the meaning of the word!' she said with a derisive laugh. 'I had my own car you know, a nice little Mini Cooper. Laurence decided we didn't need two cars and instead bought a four-by-four estate. He's very possessive of the damned thing, and only lets me drive if he comes along too. He was critical of my every manoeuvre, and made me so nervous I decided it wasn't worth it. So now I refuse to use it. Of course that means if I want to go any distance he has to drive me, and he makes it abundantly clear I'm being a "bloody nuisance".'

'What about taxis?' I asked.

'And pay with what?'

We were in a wood thick with undergrowth, and Betty suggested we take a rest on a fallen log close by. To my surprise she took a pack of cigarettes and a cheap lighter from her coat pocket.

'I didn't know you smoked!'

'I do now,' she said wryly, 'and don't tell him!'

She lit up, drew deeply on the cigarette, then breathed out a cloud of smoke with a sigh of contentment.

'Not long ago,' she said, 'I had a phone call from a woman in the village. She'd known me as a health visitor. It was a Sunday, she couldn't reach her GP, and she said she was in great pain and could I come and help her. Well, I managed to persuade Laurence to drive me to her cottage. All the way he kept saying things like, "Don't get the idea this can be a regular thing" and "I won't put up with strangers wandering around the house." I don't know where he got the idea that I wanted to set up some sort of regular practice. Anyway, on the way back I told him I'd massaged her and it had helped, it seemed to cure the pain. He repeated the word "seemed" and said it had "seemed" to work because I'd probably used my power of suggestion, and that it had nothing to do with any special power. He got quite heated. Said I had used this power of suggestion to convince him I'd saved his life, and that he'd believed it at the time. But now he knew he had slipped and fallen and simply been concussed, and he would have survived even if I hadn't been there. And then he said…' She paused, and I could sense how deeply hurt she was. 'He said it was time I accepted my so-called psychic healing was all in my mind, it was destroying our marriage, and if I didn't pull myself together he'd consider having me sectioned!'

I was totally confused. Having listened to Laurence the night before, and listening now to Betty, it was impossible to know who or what to believe.

'Section me! If it wasn't so unbelievable it would be hilarious!' She shook her head in disbelief. 'And I can't leave him. I've nowhere else to go, and he owns me, lock, stock and barrel.'

I said the only thing I could think of.

'Is there anything I can do to help?'

'Well, there is one thing you could do,' she said. 'You could persuade him to treat Toby more kindly, and allow me to have him in the house as well as letting him stay indoors at night. It's obvious from the way he accepts Crispin that it's not about Toby, it's about me. It's a way of punishing me. Will you talk to him?'

I thought for a moment.

'Of course I'll talk to him, Betty, but if you want my candid opinion, you're the only one who can change things by talking to him yourself.'

'But you've seen…'

'No, listen to me. You know Laurence; he has to feel he's the one in control. Now tell me, how badly do you want to keep Toby?'

'Need you ask?'

'And how much does it matter to you whether Laurence believes you have psychic powers or not?'

I waited before continueing. 'If you remove the target, Betty, there's no game.'

After a long moment she smiled. It was the first genuine smile I had seen since I arrived.

Lunch in the pub was pleasant enough, and the noise and banter in the crowded room made chitchat less awkward. Much to Betty's delight I had managed to persuade Laurence to allow Toby to come with us, and the two dogs lay contentedly at our feet. By the time we strolled back along the narrow road leading to the house, the weather had lifted. I had already packed our belongings into the car, and having said my goodbyes to Betty and young Toby, I gave Laurence a warm embrace.

'Before I go, Laurence, can I tell you something?'

'What's that, love?' he asked.

'It's about Crispin.'

'Oh yes?' I felt his interest fade.

'Crispin is the first dog I've ever owned, you know. As a matter of fact until he turned up I had no time for dogs. Actually, I was scared of them. Then one day he appeared in my garden. It so happened that at the time I was going through a rough patch. A rough patch mentally, I mean.'

Now I had his attention.

'I won't bore you with the details, Laurence, but just caring for him, just having him by me made all the difference and I began living in the present, instead of dwelling on the past. He literally changed me, and that changed my life.'

Laurence looked at me for a moment, then pulled me towards him in a rough hug.

'Drive carefully, you two,' he said.

I wrote my 'bread and butter' letter to the Goddards, wondering whether I had overstepped the mark, or whether anything I said might have helped. Laurence replied saying all was well and for the moment that was that. I thought of them from time to time wondering if things had changed; and then one evening a few months later my telephone rang. It was Betty.

'Sheila, forgive me for not contacting you sooner to thank you for your advice,' she said. 'Toby has grown twice the size since you saw him. He's a devoted friend and I couldn't be without him.'

I told her I was delighted to hear it, and then asked how things were between her and Laurence.

'Laurence died a week ago,' she said. 'He had another fatal attack.'

'Another?' I queried.

'Yes. Another.'

'Oh Betty, I'm so sorry,' I said, quite shaken. 'Were you with him when he died?'

'Oh yes,' she answered. 'I was. What a pity there was nothing I could do to help him.'

# CRISPIN

(The reason Crispin qualifies for this book of BASTARDS is that he was – as most dogs are – a genuine bastard. Furthermore, his mother was a bitch.)

When I started out as a professional actress, one of the things that used to irritate me was when a fellow artiste brought his or her dog along to rehearsal. Dogs were a distraction. Rehearsals were strictly for working, with no time to waste on pettings and strokings and breaks for taking them out for a leg stretch or a piddle.

I suppose the fact that I had been bitten by a dog as a child didn't exactly endear them to me; in fact I was terrified of them, and that may well have been the fault of my Lithuanian grandfather. If we were out together and a dog appeared anywhere near us, he would grab me, hold me tightly, and hiss in broken English: '*Stay still… it vill to bite you!*' Rigid with fear I would clutch him around the knees, and there we would stand, motionless, hardly daring to breath. The canny dog would sniff our dilemma (as dogs do), bark furiously at us, front paws down, tail high, until – finally realising it would get neither a good game nor a fair fight – it would slope off, keeping us frozen by throwing the odd threat over its shoulder. So terrified was I of dogs that if I happened to see one heading towards me, however far away, I would turn and walk hastily in the opposite direction, not caring how far out of my way it took me, just as long as I didn't have to risk life and limb by crossing its path. As time went by I managed to hide my phobic fear, but it never went away, and lurked within me well into adulthood.

So can you imagine how I felt when I arrived back home from a rehearsal late one afternoon, to find a dog looking in at me from the other side of my sitting-room patio doors. It seemed delighted to see me, and stood wagging its tail waiting to be let in. Yes, I was frightened, but more than that, I was furious! What on earth was it doing in my garden? Where had it come from? And how had it got in in the first place? I decided my neighbour might have the answer, particularly as the fence between our adjoining semis was badly in need of repair.

She answered the door.

'Oh, yes,' she said, 'I'm so sorry. We've taken him on. He belongs to a friend of mine who drives a delivery van for a chemist. He won't let her keep the dog with her. Unhygienic, he says. She's been leaving him with her mother during the day, but she has a cat so the dog's been locked up in a back room. She said she was thinking of putting him down but we said no, we'll keep him. Poor little thing, he's not quite a year old yet. I didn't realise he'd get into your garden... sorry about that. I'll tie him up, then he won't bother you.'

'No, no need to do that,' I said, feeling somewhat ashamed at the fuss I was making, 'just as long as he doesn't start digging about and ruining my flower beds. And by the way,' I added, trying to sound casual, 'I suppose he is quite... you know... tame, is he?'

'Oh I think so,' my neighbour said with confidence.

'Well, I hope so!' I said with no confidence, and went back indoors.

The dog was still sitting patiently outside the glass doors looking in, his head cocked to one side. Taking my courage in both hands I cautiously unlocked the doors and opened one of them just enough to get my hand through. The dog stayed put. I shut my eyes, stretched my arm slowly through the gap towards him, and waited to feel his teeth sink into my flesh. Instead I felt the smallest, most gentle of licks at my fingertips. I opened my eyes, looked at the dog and there was no doubt in my mind: he was smiling at me. Feeling just a little foolish, I smiled back. Needless to say it was the beginning of a relationship that was to change my life in every sense.

When he arrived on my patio, Crispin (for that was the name he had arrived with) had all the charm and vulnerability unmistakeable in young animals. He was, as I was to discover, almost a border collie but not quite. His fine head was black, his muzzle white, and his cheeks tan. He had two matching tan exclamation marks where his eyebrows might have been; and small tufts of untidy tan fur sprouted above each of his ebony ears, looking for all the world as though a feather had been threaded through his head from one side to the other. As for his coat, it was shiny and black and tipped with tan feathers, while the ripples that ran along his back promised in time to grow thick and curly and luxuriant. His chest was as white as the tip of his tail, and the white patches on each of his four paws made it look as though he was wearing school socks that wouldn't behave. But the most remarkable thing about Crispin was his large amber eyes. They really did seem to communicate, almost to speak... and that, coming from someone who had always considered dogs to be... well, dogs, was quite a sea change.

I had never given nor received unquestioning love, never known or understood the meaning of friendship and devotion for its own sake, and that, of course, came with time. At first I treated Crispin with caution, not sure whether to trust him or how to deal with him, and keeping him at arm's length. He, on the other hand, was patient with me and bided his time. Although it was my neighbour and her noisy, jolly twins who had 'taken him on', as time went by it became more and more clear that for them Crispin was an amusement rather than a responsibility. I would come home at all hours to find him sitting outside my patio doors, anxiously looking in. When he saw me he would turn circles of delight, waiting for me to come out and greet him. Clearly he wasn't being taken for walks, and even I knew dogs needed regular exercise. With this in mind I fashioned a lead of sorts out of some thick garden twine and, when I could, I would wind it onto his collar and walk him round the houses. To begin with these walks were intermittent but in time became more frequent, until finally I would worry if for any reason I had to let him (and myself!) down. I still had a fear of other dogs, but then I never really thought of Crispin as a dog. He was quite simply a person in his own right, and as time passed he became more and more so.

Soon I found myself buying a proper lead (I asked my neighbour 'Would you mind if I walked your dog?'), then a special wire brush ('My goodness, he does moult, doesn't he?') and inevitably picked up pamphlets and a book on dog care ('Has he had his injections? Have you wormed him? Shall I?'). I began to worry about whether he'd been fed or not, eventually deciding it might be sensible if I took on that duty as well. As you see, I was taking my 'fostering' very seriously, and my next-door neighbour, separated, and with a pair of boisterous five-year-old twins to cope with, seemed quite happy with the arrangement. The only bit of looking after now left for them was to take him in every evening, but more often than not when I got home at whatever hour, Crispin would be there, outside on the patio, and of course I had no option but to bring him in. So I did, and pretty soon he was spending his nights in my kitchen, but with the door firmly shut. Well, I wasn't having a dog wandering all over my nice clean house. Crispin complied with my house rules without a murmur, and after a while I allowed him to have the run of downstairs but no further! Sometimes I took him with me to visit friends who had their own dogs, and if friends invited me to spend weekends in the country, I would always pop next door first ('You don't mind, do you?'). But after a while I stopped asking without even thinking about it. It seemed that by some sort of osmosis Crispin had become my dog. I had a dog, and his name was Crispin, and I couldn't imagine how I'd ever managed to be without him.

We went everywhere together. Naturally I took him to rehearsals with me, and if anyone didn't approve, well, tough! They were missing out on the most loyal and undemanding of friendships. I took him with me when I worked in theatres, and I took him with me on tour. He came with me when I drove to the shops or to post letters or to visit friends, in fact everywhere whenever it was practicable. I would walk him twice a day, as well as whatever time it happened to be when I got home at night. Even if I happened to have wined and dined rather too well I would struggle out of my glittery high heels, pull on my sensible walking brogues and, hoisting up my elegant skirt, circle round the block as Crispin explored the dark secrets of the sleeping neighbourhood.

I abandoned using the lead very early on because he seemed to understand commands. He never let me out of his sight, and would come to my side when I called him. If I happened to go into a shop he would sit outside and wait, peering anxiously through the window, and when I came out, leap up at me with yelps of joy as though I'd been away on a dangerous mission with little prospect of a safe return.

In spite of this innate sense of obedience, I decided a course of dog training would do us both good, so I enrolled at a local church hall for twice-weekly evening classes. We turned up for the first session to join the queue of owners and their canine alter egos. Crispin was unimpressed. He obeyed each order like an old trouper, yawning ostentatiously while he waited his turn. As we left he gave me a withering look and sulked on the back seat all the way home. Next morning I tried him out to see what he might have remembered. He was faultless. I wasn't at all surprised. As a matter of fact I had always had a sneaky feeling that if he'd felt inclined, Crispin would have talked. He probably gave it some consideration and decided that as a means of communication it was misleading, unreliable, and frankly not worth the effort.

By now he had the run of the house. I had a dog flap put in the back door so that he could use the garden freely. He slept on my bed (or wherever else he fancied), and followed me everywhere as though we were attached by an invisible piece of string. Whenever I sat down (even on the loo) he would turn his back on me and tuck himself between my legs, demanding to be stroked. If I defaulted he would wave an imperious front paw until I resumed. If I didn't comply the waving became more insistent. This was a ploy he often used on friends and strangers, who found it irresistible, and he would con them into long sessions of stroking. The only time I remember it failing was when the prospective stroker mistook his signalling paw for a proffered handshake. 'How d'you do then, doggie!' said the poor misguided visitor as he grabbed and shook. Pulling away, 'doggie' gave him a withering look and sloped off to turn his attention to someone more his intellectual equal.

By now Crispin and I loved each other thoroughly. On the odd occasion when we weren't together I missed him hugely, and often found myself thinking, as I passed a telephone, that I ought to give him a quick ring to see if he was all right. When I did have to leave him at home, he would run upstairs and leap onto the chair that stood under my study window. From there he had a clear view of the road, and I would see him watching my car until it disappeared around the corner. What he did in the interim I will never know, but as I rounded the corner on my way home, I would always see him there, looking out. Almost immediately he would disappear, and as I drove into the carport, his beaming head and white front paws would appear over the top of the high garden gate. Somehow he must have managed to get a purchase on it with his back legs... either that, or he was dangling. I never did find out.

The only times Crispin refused point blank to communicate with me were when I was feeling miserable and in need of comfort. It so happened that when he lay curled up he fitted exactly into the circle of my arms. So when life became a burden or I felt in need of a little understanding or just a comforting cuddle, I would put my arms around him, and, if I was miserable, cry quietly into the warmth of his furry coat. Whereupon he would struggle to his feet, extricate himself from my embrace as gingerly as he could, and settle down at a distance to watch me (hopefully) pull myself together. So much for those Hollywood films where dogs lick away the tears and the pain. That, according to Crispin, was cheap sentimentality and he was having none of it.

Naturally all owners think their dogs are the brightest and the best, and I certainly plead guilty to that accusation. However, the general consensus seems to be that Crispin was remarkable. For instance, he would sit by the radio, staring at it and concentrating hard, his head cocking critically from side to side as he listened. Then again, when I had guests he would sit in one of the armchairs with his rump on the seat, his back legs dangling, and his front paws just about reaching the floor. Thus settled he would take in the conversation, giving whoever was speaking his full attention. It could be very disconcerting. His next favourite trick was to sit on the chest of anyone foolish enough to stretch out for a comfortable lie down anywhere near him. This created much hilarity, and whereas most dogs don't appreciate being laughed at, Crispin, being a born performer, loved it. He would obstinately refuse to shift, grimly adjusting his stance like a sailor on a rolling deck in rough waters. Weak with laughter, his human vessel usually gave in, and Crispin sat on, proud and victorious.

I recall the time he hurt one of his back legs and had to have it tightly bandaged. He refused to bend it or put any weight on it, but instead thrust it out sideways and tried to ignore it. Walking thus became a very comical affair, and once he realised the potential of this stunt there was no holding him. He slid, he lurched and turned circles. Embellishing his act, he glared perplexed and enraged at the offending limb. The more we laughed the more he performed, and even when his leg was cured, it only took the winding on of a 'prop' bandage and the smallest amount of persuasion to get him to give a repeat performance. After a week or so he decided it had been overplayed. One evening, friends had gathered round, the bandage was duly tied, and as we stood back and waited Crispin unpicked the knot neatly with his teeth and left the stage without a backward glance.

As a matter of fact he did appear with me on stage once, although unofficially. I was at the Phoenix Theatre in Leicester playing Adrian's mother in Sue Townsend's *The Secret Diary of Adrian Mole*. In it Adrian has a dog and, obviously inspired by Crispin's presence at rehearsals, the designer had modelled the two prop dogs on Crispin; one was a puppet that Adrian carried from time to time with his hand inside the head so that he could move it, the other was a dog-sized version on four small wheels that could be pulled across the stage and looked quite effective.

Every night Crispin would come to the theatre with me and stay in my dressing room, and I made sure that the door was firmly closed whenever I left it. On this particular night, someone must have come in after I'd gone on stage and left the door ajar, because as I sat down on the sofa and was addressing my husband, I saw the actor's face freeze. He was looking past me, so I turned and saw Crispin strolling casually across the stage towards me. Then he noticed the audience. The first row of seats was level with the stage, so he changed direction and headed towards them, beaming. He was about to engage a member of the audience in what I can only assume would have been a heavy petting session when I clicked my tongue the way riders do to gee up their horses (I never could whistle), and to my immense relief he turned, walked back to me, and (surprise, surprise) shoved his rear end into the safety of my legs, his commanding paw waving. We continued to play the scene but with absolutely no moves on my part. I stayed put on the sofa scratching Crispin's ear and praying he'd follow me offstage when I had to exit. When the cue came I leapt to my feet, ran across to the staircase, and tore up it, clicking my tongue as I went. And, good old pro that he was, Crispin followed. Unfortunately the illusion of the first floor landing ended offstage with a tiny square platform, and the only way down was via a steep wooden ladder. Crispin and I teetered together. How to get a dog down a steep ladder? Time and space were short, and it was Crispin who took the initiative. He simply leapt into the darkness. I scrambled down the wooden slats as quickly as they would allow, dreading what I might find below. What I found was… nothing. No broken dog lying in a heap, no sound of whimpering, no sign of any mishap. I headed anxiously towards my dressing room, and as I passed the prompt corner there was Crispin, his back pushed firmly against the legs of the assistant stage manager who, eyes fixed on the prompt book, was tickling his ear. Later that night as I was leaving the theatre, the unrepentant canine in tow, a member of the audience stopped me.

'Can you tell me,' she asked, 'why this dog didn't appear all the way through the play? He was so good, so well trained. Why on earth did they use those puppets instead?'

'As a matter of fact he shouldn't have gone on at all,' I told her. 'You see he's only the understudy.'

'Oh I see,' she said, and, satisfied, went on her way.

It was while I was appearing in Leicester that I happened to meet David, one of the senior members of staff in the veterinary department at the university, and whilst chatting to him I discovered that Leicester had the only centre in England where animal sperm is stored. Now not unnaturally I had contemplated the awful prospect of a time when Crispin would be no more, and as I turned this information over in my mind, I became convinced that this might well be An Answer. Crispin was such a one-off, I felt it would be a crying shame if his genes were to be lost forever, and it would solve the problem of having to find a suitable collie bitch whose owner would allow Crispin to express his interest in fathering a dynasty. Feeling somewhat self-conscious, I enquired as to whether I… well, Crispin… could take advantage of this service.

'No problem,' said David. All I had to do was to bring my dog along to the department, and once they had the resulting... result, I would pay a regular storage fee until such time as I wanted it to be used. The more I thought about it the more enthusiastic I became, and soon I was on the phone making an appointment for Crispin's Congress.

David suggested I bring him in on a Saturday morning when the campus was relatively quiet, so the next weekend I drove into the grounds, parked, and together with the imminent father of a race of canine Einsteins followed the signs to the Veterinary Section.

Crispin was happy, but not, I bet myself with a little smirk, as happy as he was likely to be when he knew what was in store for him. Down the corridor came David to meet us.

'I've got a really nice young beagle bitch just coming on heat for the first time. Follow me, my office is just along here. Come on you lucky fella!'

Crispin, ever obliging, bounded ahead. The room David showed us into was very small and very square, with a desk, a chair, a phone, and a square metre of bright green imitation grass. (I still don't understand what appeal that might have had, but then who am I?)

'Now then,' said David, warming to his task, 'I won't be a minute.' Soon he was back with the prettiest young red and white beagle bitch. I was enchanted. Crispin wasn't. He glanced at me questioningly. From a drawer David produced a large beaker and put it on the desk. The beagle bitch was manoeuvred onto the plastic grass and stood, nervous and uncertain. Crispin was pushed towards her. He bypassed the working end and they stood nose to nose.

'Come on, Crispin, you're going to love this,' said David, heaving him around and pointing him in the right direction. I smiled encouragingly, David lifted the beagle's tail. Crispin looked at me in disbelief. David shoved Crispin's head down so that his nose was within excitement-sniffing range, but Crispin dodged out of his grasp and made towards me, clearly thinking I should have discussed this with him first.

'Now come on, this won't do!' said David with determination. He made a dive at Crispin, who leapt nimbly onto the desk and backed into the corner. This, he semaphored to me, is a very private business and I have no intention of providing a floor show. I couldn't blame him, but I have to hand it to David, he did try. He cajoled, he wheedled, he pushed, he pulled. The more he did the more intransigent Crispin became.

'There's no point in going on,' I said, 'It's not going to work.'

Defeated, David sat down heavily on the chair, beaker in hand.

'Have you considered,' he asked, his breath coming in short gasps, 'that Crispin might be gay?'

Having failed as a sperm donor, I decided Crispin ought to become a father in a more dignified and conventional way: I would find him a wife. I set off for the Battersea Dogs' Home accompanied by a friend, and we toured the corridors of lost or unwanted pets. Some leapt up against the wire of the enclosures yelping as we passed, some sat hopeless and miserable watching us with large, sad eyes, others cowered at the back of their cages trembling with fear. It was impossible not to be moved, hard not to want to take them all, but I was absolutely certain I would recognise the mate meant for Crispin. And there she was: Katie. She was smaller than Crispin and, like him, not quite a border collie. Her black coat was smooth with golden feathers, and the only bit of white on her was a small circle on her chest like a medallion. I fell for her on sight, and so it seems did Crispin, and when her time was right he did his stuff valiantly and she produced six glorious pups, all boys. Crispin found them an intrusion and did his best to ignore them, but as they grew bigger and more demanding he would leap onto the nearest chair and try to frighten them off by showing his teeth and growling. They loved it, yapping and falling over each other get at him, and eventually he had, grumpily, to surrender. Eventually the pups had to be homed, and it was hard to part with them. Even harder though was choosing which pup to keep. Reluctantly I found homes for five and kept the sixth whom I named

Corbett, because he was born, as they all were, on Harry H Corbett's birthday.

What else can I tell you about the lad? Well, he had impeccable eating habits, never accepted titbits from strangers, and when offered them by friends would inspect them carefully before deciding whether they were worth eating or not... mostly not. When I gave him a digestive biscuit (his favourite), he would nibble around the edges exactly as I used to do when I was a child, only he would balance it edgewise on the floor, and keep turning it around with his paws until it was down to a coin-sized mouthful. Then he'd toss it in the air, one gulp, and it was gone. Crispin never stole food. I could leave him alone in the car with carrier bags full of the most delectable eatables, knowing he wouldn't touch any of it. Oh, and he loved swimming, shouting with excitement as he dashed along the edge of the water waiting for me to throw something in for him to retrieve.

He never seemed to do anything just for its own sake, he needed a reason. If anyone appeared less than enthusiastic about dogs he had a great instinct for respecting their weakness. He would pretend to ignore them, but watch carefully until they seemed to feel safe with him. Then he would casually wander at some distance, then sit with his back towards them, wander again getting imperceptibly closer, until the unsuspecting target would find a warm, furry body sitting within hand stroking distance and looking up at them with liquid amber eyes. It never failed.

Considering my grandfather's fear of dogs it was understandable that my mother wasn't too keen on canines either. The first time she came to stay with Crispin in the house, she put up with him for my sake, but kept a respectable distance from him. He accepted her right to treat him with caution and never foisted himself on her and the truce held, until one morning a week or so after she arrived I happened to pass her open bedroom door, and found her sitting on the edge of the bed with Crispin characteristically leaning against her legs. My mother was running her fingers cautiously through his shiny coat with a look of wonder on her face.

'So soft!' she said, 'I've never felt live fur before!' Crispin looked at me, and I swear he winked.

Crispin died at the remarkable age of nineteen. He was frail and confused, and resentful of the limitations senility imposed on him. I put off the desperate decision as long as I could, but one day, as he lay on my bed, I sat beside him and looked into his eyes, now clouded with age, and it was quietly agreed between us. The two veterinary nurses arrived soon after. He was still lying on my bed, asleep. I held him in the circle of my arms and buried my face in his fur to avoid seeing the final needle. Crispin stirred, gave a small sneeze, and was gone.

He lies snug at the bottom of my garden under a slab of York stone. On it stands a low carved plant pot with trailing ivy, and a fern whose leaves spray upwards like a fountain. On the stone is a brass plaque engraved with his name and the date of the day we met, and the date that he died. Crispin changed me and he changed my life, and to him I owe the deepest gratitude for the life-affirming company of the dogs that followed him. I miss him still, and still I shed a tear from time to time. But then I remember how we once saw the New Year in together, sitting side by side on tall stools in an almost deserted bar in Manchester. In front of me was a glass of cheap, flat champagne, in front of Crispin a wide, shallow ashtray of water. And as the barman's tinny radio chimed the old year out and the new year in, I hugged my dog, and felt hugely proud that against all the odds, Crispin had chosen me.

# DIRTY LIZ

Down a dark alley hidden from view
Lives a bad dog and a cat that won't mew.

There in a dustbin (so I've been told)
Lives dirty Liz who is terribly old.

When it rains they never feel it
'Cause there ain't no sky
To tell them if it's wet or dry
But there in that alley the three of them is

Liz cat and bad dog
Cat dog and Liz.

# A BASTARD HAPPENING

It was just a regular day in London town, cold and grey and raining. I resisted the temptation to give my young dog Oscar's regular walk a miss and stay indoors to watch a talk-show host verbally abuse members of the public (who deserve all they get and seem to enjoy it). Instead, taking a large umbrella and pulling on a pair of stout boots, I bundled the small dog into the back of my car, and set off for a footpath that circles a local reservoir where swans and ducks abound, and small scuttling animals attract the interest of hovering birds. Here the undergrowth is thick enough to excite the interest of the laziest of canines, and Oscar was in his element.

I parked my car as usual on a patch of old tarmac at the side of a rugby field that flanks the reservoir, and set off. As we came to the end of our circuit, the heavens opened. Fortunately I had taken my umbrella with me, but my dog, reluctant to end the walk at the best of times, stood at some distance from the car and refused to budge. No wheedling or cajoling could overcome his stubbornness, and so, stifling my instinct to yell at the fur-soaked brat, and knowing that chasing would only exacerbate matters, I abandoned the umbrella, and crouched down holding out a bag of the treats I keep in my pocket for such occasions. Slowly, reluctantly, he crept towards me, while the rain trickled down inside my jacket and plastered my hair to my scalp. When his nose touched my hand I made a grab for his collar, slung him into the back of the estate and slammed the lid shut. I ran around to the passenger-side door, opened it, and threw the bag of treats and my car key onto the seat. And as I slammed the door shut, for some inexplicable reason the automatic lock activated itself and, with a warning beep, instantly rendered the car impenetrable. Now, the only way my car can be locked is by pressing a button on the key (a small oblong of plastic, roughly the size of two squares of a thick chocolate bar), and as I hadn't pressed it, I could only assume that the vibration of the slamming door must have triggered the mechanism. That, or the Guardian Bastard who plagues my life was enjoying another of his japes. Either way, I was well and truly screwed.

Picture the scene. There I am in a heavy rainstorm on a cold, late January afternoon; with an umbrella, I grant you, but with no means of getting into my car, which happens to be the only vehicle parked on a secluded site, hidden from the road, somewhere on the north side of London. Inside the car is a small, nine-month-old dog, wide-eyed and shivering and soaked to the skin. What to do? I can't phone for help because I haven't brought my mobile phone with me. This is not unusual. I dislike its smallness, its mean reluctance to open its resistant jaws, the tiny buttons that defy my fingers, and the maddening beeps that usually herald junk messages. Should I try to break a window? Even if I could find a brick I doubt it would even so much as chip the glass of a car designed by Germans.

Then I remember that in one of my desk drawers I have a box of spare keys, and I'm sure I've seen a replica of my car key in there. Or have I? Please God, let there be a replica of my car key in there! I'll have to flag down a car and... what? I can't exactly ask for a lift home. Ask them to phone the roadside rescue service I sign up to every year? Maybe I could ask *them* to give me a lift home. Or perhaps they'd know how to break into the car without actually... breaking into the car. As it were. Well, they must be used to this sort of thing. I head for the roadside and stand waving my arms in semaphore, only too aware of how ridiculous I must look, and how unlikely it is that anyone will stop. I sure as hell wouldn't!

I'm not wrong, but at last a car does slow down. It is a small car into which five Asian women of varying sizes and ages are packed. The driver leans across the passenger beside her the better to hear me, and from under my umbrella I try to explain, asking if she could do me an enormous favour and phone the rescue service for me. Do I have the number? Of course I don't have the number. The card with their number is in my car. I suggest that maybe she could phone her mobile's directory enquiries and... She shakes her head. I go on flagging.

A heart-stopping moment when I remember my house keys are also locked in the car, and then remember my neighbour has a set. I can only pray she'll be in. I close the umbrella and go back to waving at the few passing vehicles. Another small car stops. Another Asian driver, a man this time, with a male passenger beside him and in the back a large woman I presume to be his wife. I pour out my woes and surprise myself by sounding hysterical. Calm down, he says several times, poor man, and tells me that although it's out of his way, he will take me to a minicab firm just up the road. Hyperventilating I get in beside the woman, my wet clothes and dripping umbrella doing her no favours, and she shifts away from me with distaste.

After a few interminable minutes I say agitatedly to the driver: I thought you said the minicab firm was close by! He replies, We'll be there soon. After another few minutes I ask: Are we there yet? Soon, says the driver. The minutes drag and I begin to regret accepting his offer. It's miles away! I say. You said we'd be there soon, twice! The driver brakes hard. You want to get out? No, no! I bleat, I'm sorry. Sorry. For no apparent reason I begin to sob. No tears, just the noise. What is happening to me? At last he pulls up and points at a minicab sign on a forecourt. I tumble out burbling thank you and sorry and burst into the tiny office where a couple of Asian men are drinking tea and smoking. I know I look like a loony old woman who is out of control but that's exactly what I am. I need a cab now! I shriek, now! I need to get key… left dog… rugby by reservoir… my words tumble out senselessly. A portly man with a kind face under his beard stands up. I'll take you, he says. I give him my address. He knows the way. I skip-hop with him to his car, clamber into the passenger seat, and getting a grip at last, explain the situation. The plan is for him to get me home to (hopefully) pick up the spare key and then drive me back to my car and the incarcerated dog. I decide it's the dog that has made me behave so uncharacteristically, even though logic tells me he's not likely to die of malnutrition or heat or suffocation; the worst that can happen is he might attempt digging his way out, or gnaw bits off the tasty leather seats.

My Asian driver is a godsend. Not only does he listen sympathetically, but he chooses the back streets to avoid the traffic. We're at my house, my neighbour's car is outside, she is inside, I unlock the front door, rush to my desk, find the box of keys, turn it out onto a chair, and… no car key. There are door keys and drawer keys and suitcase keys and latch keys, there are keys that have no purpose whatsoever, but a car key? No. Of course not.

I decide to phone the RAC. With a rising sense of panic I find their number in my address book, and after the usual identity questions the woman asks, where exactly is the car? Now I have no idea of the name of the road where my car can be located, but I tell her I do know it is somewhere off the Edgware Road, and there can't be that many reservoirs off the Edgware Road, now can there? Sorry madam, I need the name of the road. Yes, but I don't know it! I am getting distressed. Suddenly the name of the reservoir comes to me! The Welsh Harp, I tell her, it's called the Welsh Harp. Is that a pub? No, it's the name of the reservoir and I'm parked next to it next to a rugby field that's next to it. Now the frenzied old lady syndrome has kicked in. Calm down madam, says the woman, I can't help you unless you give me some specific information. But there's a dog! I wail. A dog! Is it dangerous? Good God, no, it's a pup, a puppy! Look madam, she says, I can't help you if you're going to shout at me. Sorry, sorry, her reprimand has brought me somewhat to my senses. Wait, I say, I'll look it up in my A-to-Z map of London. I find the road. It's called Cool Oak Lane, I tell her, triumphant. Pool...? No, Cool, Cool as in cold. Cooool! She finds it and then tells me it will take up to two hours for someone to get to me. Two hours! You cannot be serious! It's getting dark, I whimper, it's pouring with rain, I'm parked in a remote, secluded spot, and my dog's been in the car for at least two hours. Surely you have emergency services to rush to the aid of an old, defenceless woman who might at any moment be robbed or raped or murdered even! The woman is unmoved. I quite understand, madam, she says calmly, however we're very busy. It will still take up to two hours to get to you. I grab my mobile and my wallet and rush out of the house, back to the minicab driver and tell him I can't find the keys. No problem, says my saviour, if you have a wire coat-hanger and a couple of big screwdrivers I can fix it. Well, I happen to have a large collection of screwdrivers but no wire coat-hangers, because I always junk them. My saviour seems to have caught my adrenalin rush and we speed away with me clutching a pair of screwdrivers, scanning the shops for a dry cleaners. He spots one just after the Cool Oak turning, skids to a stop, reverses, U-turns, and I leap out. The startled owner hands over one wire hanger and I burble my gratitude and leap back into the cab.

The rain had stopped. My lone car was still there, the dog looked miserable, and from what I could see the interior was still intact. The key ring with its plastic oblong was lying tantalisingly on the passenger seat, and the next half hour was spent trying to prise open the window. Using the two screwdrivers my Asian friend eventually managed to pull the top of the window ever so slightly away from its frame. Following his instructions I took over to keep up the pressure and, as we stood head to head, he fed the straightened hanger hook-first through the tiny gap. To my astonishment, after painstaking perseverance he actually managed to hook the ring attached to the key, and began carefully to pull it upwards. Holding my breath I watched it reach the gap, then saw the block, too large for the narrow opening, drop to the floor, out of sight. As the man removed the screwdrivers from the window I noted stoically the dents in the metal and the distorted bend of the frame.

I thanked him, gave him forty pounds (which was all I had with me) and, telling him I'd be fine, said there was no need for him to hang around while I waited for the rescue team. It was getting dark, I was shivering, and my gloveless arthritic hands were seizing up. I had two hours to wait. I peered in at Oscar who looked back at me resentfully. The only bench at the side of the pitch was waterlogged, so I began to pace around the tarmac to keep warm. And as I paced it came to me that I *did* have a spare car key at home. It was in a bowl on my kitchen table, kept there for exactly this sort of emergency, never needed and subsequently forgotten. I didn't like myself.

I dialled the RAC, cancelled the call-out asking for a taxi instead, and after a long half-hour it came, a warm, dry minicab, about to take me home and return me post haste with the key. I explained the need to hurry, and the car swooped over the flyover, coming to a sudden grinding halt as a severe traffic jam stretched endlessly ahead. Nothing was moving. It was clear nothing was likely to move, and I began to keen like an old washerwoman.

'What are you crying for?' asked my most recent Asian driver. 'It won't do any good.'

'Look, you drive and I'll cry,' I told him, and returned to my tearless wailing.

Then I noticed a road I was sure I had used to bypass the main road.

'You see that road up there on the right? Well, if we ever get to it, turn in. It's a quick way to get past the traffic.'

'No,' said the driver, 'I know what I'm doing.'

'Listen. I've lived here for years and if you go down that road…'

'I never listen to my passengers,' he said flatly.

'Well maybe you should!' I snapped and slumped back in a sulk.

As we snailed towards the road I had indicated, the man at the wheel spoke.

'Okay,' he said. 'Just this once.'

'Great! Excellent!'

I sat forward in excited anticipation, and when we finally drew parallel, 'Now!' I said feverishly, 'turn into it now!'

He turned into it.

'Take the next left!'

He took the next left.

'Now right and then left!'

He turned right and then he turned left and then... we found ourselves in someone's driveway. We were in a cul de sac. The driver turned off the engine. All was silent except for his heavy breathing. At last he spoke.

'Now get out,' he said.

'No no! Please don't leave me! I'm sorry I'm sorry I'm so so sorry!'

Any sense of dignity had flown; I was living out a nightmare.

'Not *you* get out. *I* will now get out my satnav.'

As he reversed, I found myself running my hands through my hair like they do in the movies. Now I understood why.

His satnav took us straight back into the traffic jam, but did I care? I sat back, calm and peaceful. There was nothing more I could do. And I didn't mind. As far as I was concerned it was all over.

And so I picked up the elusive key, along with some money to pay the driver who drove me back to the reservoir. Oscar refused to come out of the car, so I left him cowering where he was. Then I struggled my stiff, cold hands into my driving gloves, and as I headed home, I wondered idly where along the way I had abandoned my umbrella.

# HOW DARE THE BASTARD!

There is a postal sorting office I pass regularly on my way home, outside of which stands a larger than usual Royal Mail post box. This particular box offers more pickups than usual, as well as a Sunday clearing, and this makes it popular with folk who are keen to have their correspondence dealt with quickly. One day, anxious to get a letter off, I pulled my car up next to the box, picked up the letter and, turning off the engine, hopped out, foolishly leaving the key in the ignition. It took no more than ten or so seconds to post it, and as I turned back, to my horror I saw a biker in full black leather gear complete with helmet and visor, opening the door of my car and about to get into the driving seat! Without thinking of the consequences I ran towards the car, and just managed to get a foot onto the ledge of the door when the bastard, already in the driving seat, turned the key. The engine started, and as he accelerated away I found myself close by him, hanging onto the rim of the roof with my left hand, my left foot just inside the car, and clutching the half-open door behind me with my right hand, my right foot dragging along the tarmac as the car picked up speed.

Now it's true time slows down on such occasions, and while I yelled at the driver to stop, I wondered almost casually why on earth any of the oncoming traffic didn't do something to stop us. Why didn't they, for instance, immediately drive over the centre white line and pull across the front of us like they do in action films. And presumably write off both cars like they do in action films.

After speeding for a couple of blocks the carjacker suddenly braked.

'Get out!' he shouted.

Instead of feeling relief and gratitude and taking advantage of his offer, I thought: *How bloody dare the bastard! This is MY bloody car!* I stayed put, and he took off again, accelerating harder than before and weaving from side to side in an effort, I supposed, to throw me off my perch. This only made me tighten my grip. By now I was getting used to the ride. I looked up at the road ahead and the rush of cold air was quite refreshing. Then I took a look at the man at the wheel and noticed there was a gap in his visor where his eyes should have been. Could I poke my fingers through it and blind him? Logic told me that blinding a man who was driving at speed wouldn't be very sensible, so instead I resorted again to screaming.

'Help me!' I shrieked to no one in particular, 'help me!'

And as I shrieked, I remembered how a woman had recently been killed when she'd thrown herself onto the bonnet of her car as a man attempted to drive it away. Now reality hit me and I was terrified.

'You're going to kill me!' I yelled over and over again, and wonder whether that thought had crossed the driver's mind because he suddenly hit the brake and the car skidded to a halt. Out of nowhere a heavy duty crimson motorbike roared up beside me.

'Get on!' shouted its rider, revving the powerful engine. The carjacker pushed past me, leapt onto the pillion, and they were gone.

I sank down on the recently vacated seat. My right foot hurt a little, and for some unaccountable reason I found myself gently wheezing. It was oddly comforting. Then a young man came round and said he'd called the police on his mobile. He asked how I was, and finding I was none the worse for the experience, told me he had managed to note down the motorbike's number. A police car arrived remarkably quickly, and I was quite peeved when the two officers ignored me and proceeded to question the small crowd who had witnessed the event. After all it was my party! Eventually they did get round to checking me out, explaining they had wanted to get all the information they could before any witnesses disappeared.

Was I all right? Yes, I was fine; and after listening to my story, instead of praising me for my presence of mind, he muttered, 'Silly woman!' An ambulance appeared, they checked my foot and came to the conclusion that I'd probably cracked a bone and all it needed was strapping up, and the policeman offered to drive me home but I declined.

And that was how I came to be driving home (carefully watching my speed) followed by a police car and an ambulance. With me sitting on a kitchen chair, a paramedic strapped up my foot and a policeman took down my statement; and a few weeks later the same policeman came by to tell me they had traced the motorbike. Unfortunately it was one used by a gang of villains and, as I couldn't identify the culprit, it was impossible to know exactly which of them it was who had taken me for that memorable ride.

# EVERARD

*So he's chucked you over and you're finally free of him?*

I know. Isn't it wonderful?

*But you still can't get over him in spite of all he put you through?*

I know. Isn't it ridiculous?

*I can't believe it! It's obvious he enjoyed making you miserable.*

He did, you're absolutely right, he did.

*Hey! Watch what you're doing with that bottle, it's too good to waste! Pass it here… let me do it.*

Thanks. That's a really nice drop.

*Tell me, Stella, what on earth did you see in him? He's such a snob, such an arrogant bastard, and, for goodness' sake, putting it politely, he's not exactly a picture, is he?*

I know, I know. But he's a charmer.

*As in snake!*

No, be fair, whatever you may think of him, he has charm. It overrides his looks. There's something about him that everyone falls for. Everyone.

*Not me! It sure as hell passed me by. I sensed there was something dodgy about him the minute I met him.*

Ah, but the circumstances were different. You'd invited him over to dinner.

*No, get it straight. I invited you over to dinner and suggested you might want to bring your current 'affair' with you so that Arthur and I could look him over.*

Jane, you can be so blunt!

*How about substituting 'blunt' with 'honest'? Speaking as a devoted if distant cousin of yours, I am ever hopeful that you might find a reasonably acceptable male with scruples rather than one of your usual chauvinistic sods...*

Hey!

*I'm not telling you anything you don't know already. Let's face it, your track record reads like a Who's Who of bad casting, and this one was a real star!*

Oh, come on. Everard may be flawed, but he has a lot of redeeming qualities.

*For instance?*

Well, he knows a lot about wine and he taught me to appreciate it. For instance, I recognise this isn't just supermarket plonk we're drinking here. It's a rich Burgundy probably located somewhere in the...

*...Brent Cross area. And you're right, it's not just any wine, it's M&S wine, so do me a favour and stop knocking it back without actually tasting it.*

Sorry. And he improved my vocabulary. For instance, you don't say 'wealthy', you say 'rich'. And it's not 'lounge', it's 'sitting room'. And he showed me how to cut cheese.

*I'm impressed. How do you cut cheese?*

You cut it like a cake, so that everyone gets a bit of the middle.

*Thank you. I feel all the better for knowing that.*

And he advised me about how to behave in social situations. For instance, if he were to take me to a dinner party and I didn't know what the person sitting next to me was talking about, instead of pretending I did, I was to say: 'I don't quite understand what you're saying, but my job as an actress is to observe, and I love the way you hold your fork'.

*Blimey! Did it work?*

I never got the chance to find out. I don't know why we're laughing.

*We're laughing because he manipulated you by talking you into believing a load of guff! You and how many others? He even managed to talk five hundred pounds out of Arthur.*

Arthur? Your Arthur?

*That's right. My highly successful businessman husband Arthur was taken to the cleaners by your erstwhile lover Everard.*

I didn't know Arthur knew him!

*He didn't until you brought him here for dinner.*

Wait a minute, I'm totally confused! Why didn't you tell me?

*Because you were so besotted with the man I didn't want to add to your woes.*

Thanks, that makes me feel a whole lot better. How about telling me now?

*Apparently after dinner that night, Everard the Ever-Ready told Arthur about some sort of amazingly lucrative deal he was on to, and suggested that if it interested him they might meet for lunch the following week at the White Elephant to discuss Arthur's investing in it.*

And Arthur went?

*Arthur went.*

Since you told me you sensed something dodgy about him I'm surprised you didn't warn Arthur against going.

*Arthur's pretty shrewd, he doesn't need my advice. All I did was point out that Everard had doubtless taken note of the tasteful contents of our house, not to mention the size of our property. Anyway, when he got back from the lunch Arthur told me how fascinated he'd been observing Everard work his charm.*

There! You see?

*It seems Everard had the restaurant manager falling over himself to please him and it spread to the waiters like an epidemic. The wine waiter nearly wet his pants when Everard declared a bottle of vintage wine 'corked'. To quote Arthur, the entire restaurant held its collective breath as they waited for Everard's verdict on the replacement, and when he nodded his approval there was an audible sigh of relief.*

That sounds like the man I know and love. Or don't know and wish I didn't love. He used to take me out to lunch in posh restaurants, you know. He'd vet what I wore, never trousers, always skirts, that kind of thing. Oh, and muted colours or he wouldn't go out with me. Mind you, I loved dressing up and acting sophisticated. I was never sure what to order so he would order for me. As a matter of fact he took me to the White Elephant once. It should have been a real treat, but he was in one of his meaner moods, and all I did was cry into my plate of pasta while he made cruel remarks about my appearance. A waiter was hovering nearby trying to eavesdrop, and when Everard noticed him, he turned up the volume. I think I'm going to cry all over again…

*No you're not! You know, one of the most maddening things about your associating with that bastard is that he seems to have excised your sense of humour! I mean, looked at objectively, the scene you've just recounted is hilarious!*

To you, maybe!

*See what I mean?*

I bet Arthur didn't find it humorous to be conned out of five hundred pounds.

*As a matter of fact Arthur may not have found it amusing, but he did say that Everard's performance had been so admirable it had almost been worth every penny!*

There you are! People are intrigued by him. Do you know, whenever we went to a 'do' he'd chat up the guests, and inevitably they would give him their business cards or write their details on scraps of paper so that he'd keep in touch.

*And where at this 'do' were you while he was social climbing?*

Oh, I was there, but I was instructed to circulate on my own. Off he'd go and leave me to 'circulate' which I was useless at, and I would end up sitting in a corner on my own with an idiotic smile on my face, pretending to be hugely interested in something on the other side of the room and nursing the same glass he'd handed me when he set off on his rounds.

*If you hated it all so much, why on earth did you go?*

Because, dear cousin, whenever I was summoned, even at a moment's notice, I would dive into my car and play chauffeur. Apart from finding it flattering to be asked, I wanted to be with him. I suppose the worst call-out I had was driving him to Rules restaurant in Covent Garden, and being ordered to wait outside in the car while he enjoyed a leisurely two-hour lunch with one of his 'prospects'.

*And you waited?*

Need you ask?

*Well, did he at least bring you a doggy bag?*

Yes. But he kept it for his supper.

*Now there's a surprise. How did Everard pay for this high lifestyle of his? Or was it simply by conning money out of gullible folk?*

I never did find out. But I remember being in his flat when a young man of about eighteen was with him in his so-called office. The poor boy was weeping. I gathered Everard had involved him in some sort of deal, and was demanding he clear out his savings account and hand over the proceeds. Apparently he was saving up for college and it was all he had. I could tell Everard was enjoying it.

*Poor kid! I hope you never gave Everard any money... did you? Don't tell me you gave him money?*

No, of course not. Not as such.

*What do you mean, not as such?*

Well, not for any deals or anything like that. But from time to time he'd just sort of... get money out of me.

*For instance?*

There was the time he sent for me to join him in Geneva...

*I didn't know you'd been to Geneva.*

Strictly speaking I haven't.

*I'm confused.*

Well, he met me at the airport and immediately bundled me into his hire car and headed for the Alps. All I saw of Geneva was a distant view from the top of a mountain when he pulled over to a siding.

*That was thoughtful of him.*

No it wasn't. He only stopped because he was feeling randy.

*Hang on, are you saying... what I think you're saying?*

Probably. Look, there I was alone with him up a mountain and I hadn't seen him for a while and I was in love and I'd missed him and he made me feel sexy whenever we were together. If I'm honest, it was probably that that kept our affair going.

*Aha! Now we have it.*

Yup, I guess we have.

*So there you are up a mountain, as it were. Spare me the details! What then?*

He suggested I hand over my money and traveller's cheques for safe keeping. Then it was over the Alps and into Italy.

*Sounds like good old-fashioned highway robbery.*

You're not wrong. When we stopped at a wayside auberge for lunch he made me sign one of my traveller's cheques to pay for it. And then on the way out he sneaked a bottle off the end of the counter and slipped it under his jacket!

*More highway robbery!*

I asked him why he'd done it and he said, 'For fun!' Mind you, justice was served when he opened it. It turned out to be undrinkable.

*Against my better judgement, I am developing a sense of admiration for your Everard. He really is something!*

I'll drink to that. Fancy a top up?

*No, you carry on, I'll sit this one out.*

Look, I know you think I should be grateful he's turned his gimlet eye onto some other poor female, but I can't seem to get him out of my system. And he wasn't always assertive and unkind, you know. We had some fun together, and as long as I did what he asked he could be amusing and even affectionate.

*Like rewarding a grateful pet with treats for doing what it's been trained to do?*

That was below the belt! Anyway I couldn't help doing whatever he wanted me to, because I was in his thrall.

*In his thrall. Hmmm. I've always wondered what a thrall is exactly.*

I've no idea, but I sure as hell know what it's like to be in someone's.

*Top me up, I've changed my mind. Thanks. You've never told me how you met him.*

Oh. I met him at a party given by this woman who used to temp for my agent. She decided it would be amusing to have an actress and a bishop at a charity evening she was giving, and she invited me to be the token actress. The closest she could get to a bishop was a dishy young priest who played a really mean jazz piano.

*A dishy young priest who played jazz piano!*

It's absolutely true, and he was sensational. Anyway, I spent most of the evening sitting on the piano stool beside him and singing along from time to time. And then I saw Everard. He was leaning against the fireplace in what I can only describe as a studied pose, pretending to listen to our hostess, but it was clear she was boring him rigid. Anyway, there was something about him…

*Oh Lord, here we go!*

Yup, there I went.

*That's my girl. Sensing danger you made a beeline for him.*

That's about the size of it.

*How long ago was that?*

About three years.

*Three years! Dear Lord! Tell me, when you chatted him up did you write your details on a piece of paper and hand it over to add to his collection of pickings?*

No, I was much more creative. I asked if he enjoyed the theatre and said I happened to have two complimentary tickets for a West End play.

*And you were lying.*

I was lying.

*You bought the tickets the next day.*

I bought the tickets the next day.

*And he went.*

He came.

*And afterwards, where did you take him for dinner?*

All right, smart arse. I took him to Joe Allen's.

*To impress him because that's where all the West End actors go.*

Not all.

*And was he duly impressed?*

No. Disappointingly the staff knew him better than they knew me!

*Ah.*

But what really surprised me was when he told me he was a New Zealander! He spoke with such a cut-glass accent you'd never have guessed it.

*Oh Stella, Stella, surely that must have been a dead giveaway? Even you should have realised you were well out of your depth?*

Wait, there's more. He told me he was a freelance journalist, that he'd been married twice, had no children, and at the moment had a sixteen-year-old girl living with him!

*Living with an underage girl?*

He told me he'd rescued her from a tragic family situation, and before you jump to conclusions he assured me there was no sex involved.

*Oh come on! And you believed him?*

I believed him.

*Stella!*

Well, I wanted to believe him! Anyway, we started spending time together and one thing led to another and it… blossomed…

*Not a word I'd have chosen. And where was the sixteen-year-old all this time?*

Well, Everard was adamant that Tilly… that's her name… that Tilly wasn't to know what was going on, so I never actually stayed the night at his flat. Anyway there was only one bedroom and one large bed. Tilly kept a ghastly little teddy bear on it, probably as a reminder to him that she was still a child. She was very possessive about him. She used to sit on his lap and it looked ridiculous – I mean she was what you might call 'bonny' – but he seemed to find it quite disarming.

*Disarming and disabling I shouldn't wonder, having a large post-pubescent female crushing your manhood! But I'm intrigued. If yours was, as you imply, a blossoming affair, when and where did it flower?*

At his flat during the day when Tilly was out. Or if he decided to stay the night at my place he would bring Tilly with him. They'd go to bed together in my spare room, and when she was asleep he'd…

*Stella! Are you telling me this canny sixteen-year-old didn't know what was going on?*

Of course she knew, and I knew she knew, and I'm pretty sure Everard knew she knew, and that I knew she knew.

*Hold it! And don't speak until I've had a large swallow. Right. You may speak.*

She's a canny little minx, is Tilly. Probably the only female Everard had any respect for. Apart from his mother.

*Is she still around?*

No. About a year ago Everard introduced her to his younger brother who was over from New Zealand, and she upped and married him.

*No!*

Everard's core was well and truly shaken.

*Hooray! So for the last year or so you've had Everard to yourself?*

Not exactly. I knew he had a few other acolytes on the go, but I could never prove it.

*Tell me something, apart from the thrall thing, give me one good reason why you stayed with him. Was it the sex? You did say it was pretty fantastic.*

Since you ask, sex with Everard was indeed pretty fantastic. However, there was one teensy drawback. He never kissed me.

*I don't think I heard you correctly. Did you say he never kissed you?*

That's what I said.

*Not ever?*

Not ever. Not even by mistake. He said it was an intimacy too far because it involved his head.

*So he did know where his lips were?*

Apparently. And then one time when he came back from an assignment in the Philippines, he told me he'd had a fling with one of the native girls, and while he was kissing her, he'd thought about the possibility of kissing me.

*And?*

And that was it. He just thought about it. Did I tell you that he was convinced I was sleeping with other men?

*And were you?*

No.

*Pity.*

But he wouldn't believe me. Then one evening Everard had to wine and dine an elderly and prestigious Canadian film critic, and to my surprise he asked me to go with him. After dinner we took this man back to his hotel, and we were sitting in the lounge having a nightcap when Everard asked him if he'd like to spend the night with me!

*You're kidding!*

I was shocked and humiliated, but I didn't want to hurt the old bloke's feelings…

*Oh spare me!*

So I sort of laughed it away. I think the poor man was as embarrassed as I was, but Everard was furious with me. As we left he told me I'd let me down.

*Can we have a moment's silence? Just pass the bottle, will you.*

Certainly.

*I can't help wondering... while you were devoting your life to pleasing Everard, what on earth was happening to your career?*

Spiralling downwards. I turned down lots of offers, but I didn't care. I couldn't bear to be out in case I missed his calls.

*No mobile phones in them days, eh?*

Just as well! I'd have been even more of a nervous wreck!

*You know, if you had put as much dedication into your career as you put into your love life...*

Don't tell me! Mind you I wasn't the only actress whose career he screwed...

*In every sense!*

A few months ago, just as I was about to go into an Equity meeting, I saw this ex-girlfriend of his. We got chatting and I tell you, I seem to have escaped quite lightly! She got pregnant by him, and when she told him he accused her of sleeping with a friend of his at the same time so she couldn't be sure it was his.

*And had she?*

Of course not! She told me she'd considered going through with it, but did she really want to have a child of his? You can see her point! Anyway, she had a swift termination, and when she phoned to tell him he said: 'Dear girl, if only you'd told me Tilly and I would have come to visit you in the clinic.'

*He really is a nasty piece of work.*

At one point I was so miserable I made an attempt to drag some sympathy out of him by swallowing a handful of sleeping pills in front of him.

*You what!*

And I happened to drop a few on the floor. He picked them up and handed them back to me.

*Stella, for God's sake…*

Calm down! It may have been a large gesture but it was a small dose and I was fine. I just went to bed and when I woke up I'd lost a day.

*You were bloody lucky!*

I know. I've never told any of this to anyone before, Jane, and I'm getting a sense of perspective. I can't believe how weak-minded I've been!

*Hallelujah! The scales have fallen from her eyes! About bloody time!*

But the most ridiculous thing I allowed myself to be put through was when Everard persuaded me to take up golf… a game I have always considered boring and pointless.

*You and me both.*

Nonetheless, golf was one of Everard's pleasures and one at which he naturally excelled, so I would play caddy and stagger around the golf course after him hauling his bag of clubs. Then one day he suggested I learn to play. 'Dear girl, not only would I have someone handy to play against, but the male members of the club would find the sight of you in a little tartan skirt and white ankle-socks a real turn-on. It would certainly turn me on!' he said, and of course that was it. For the next few weeks I fought a losing battle between a set of clubs I'd begged off an ex-golfing friend and that nasty little white ball. I'm left-handed, the clubs happened to be right-handed, and when I pointed this out to Everard he beamed and said, 'Dear girl, what a gift! that means you'll have an advantageously strong pull-through!' It never occurred to me to ask that if that was the case, why didn't right-handed people play left-handed?

Anyway I persisted, my golfing instructor persisted, the divots flew and I wept with frustration. And then one day I was summoned to chauffeur him to pick up his newly serviced car from a garage on the outskirts of London. And he ordered me to bring my clubs with me, because there was a nine-hole golf course on the way where we could stop off.

*I can guess what's coming.*

No you can't. So we reach the golf course. Everard sets off towards the golf shop while I haul my hated canvas bag out of the boot and follow him. He stops at the door. 'Come on,' he calls, and then he looks at me and says 'Dear girl, you're shivering!' And I am. I'm freezing, because in order to please my sartorially demanding lord and master, I am wearing a thin chiffon blouse and an equally lightweight skirt… not exactly suitable for a round of anything on this frosty autumn morning. I smile weakly and say through chattering teeth, no, no, I'm fine. 'Nonsense,' he says, 'follow me.'

So into the shop we go. Everard strides up to the counter where a bored young man is sitting reading a paperback, and behind him the wall is decorated with golfing paraphernalia including several sweaters which are pinned up in unlikely positions. Everard looks them over. 'What do you think of that one over there, dear girl?' he asks. 'That one there, on the far left.' He points. Well, it isn't quite what I'd have chosen for myself, but hey! it looks as though Everard is actually about to buy me something! This man who has never given me so much as a chocolate bar, who has never reimbursed me, neither for food nor fuel, this man is finally going to show me not only some consideration, but is also about to render up some of his very own money and buy me a sweater! I tell you, Jane, I felt humbled, and ashamed that I'd misjudged him all this time… No! Don't you dare interrupt!

'Very nice,' I said, trying to sound sincere.

'That's the one, then,' said Everard. The lad behind the counter asked what size. 'Let's have a look first,' said Everard.

The lad opened a drawer, took out a similar sweater and handed it to Everard who inspected it. 'What do you think?'

'Very nice!' I managed, trying to control my emotions.

'Splendid!' said Everard.

Then he struggled out of his worn-out sweater, and handed it to me saying, 'You can borrow that until we get back to my flat.'

*Sorry, but I saw that coming. And then?*

Then I walked round the course wearing his sweater, barely able to see through my tears and chopping out clumps of earth with my right-handed clubs.

*I hate to bring this up, but has it crossed your mind that getting you to play with the wrong clubs might have been sabotage?*

Good God! Of course! The bastard! How he must have chortled! If I'd realised it at the time I could finally have put those iron-tipped sticks to good use and clubbed him to death!

*Using your left hand, of course.*

Of course!

*Ah well, another day, another bottle. What do you say?*

# REGRETTE RIEN

(To be sung to the tune of *Je Ne Regrette Rien*... with sincere apologies to the great chanteuse Edith Piaf)

No, no more sex
Sex is a no-no, an ex
Only friends,
No more mates
No more angst
Watching calendar dates.

I can't believe
How till now
I could be so naïve
Men can screw
All they like
You refuse, and they'll call you a dyke.

They say love is a game
But the odds aren't the same.
Men can chance it and lie
Leaving us high and dry.
As I look at my past
From the first to the last
Every man I adored
Has been mentally flawed.

*Don't Ask Me!*

So, no more pain,
No, no more messing my brain
Fingers crossed
Legs are too
I just pray
No more Bastards are due!